'You're beautif[...] hoarsely. 'So b[...]

And, for the first time in her life, Emily actually felt that she was. She didn't feel awkward or self-conscious as she often did when she modelled. She didn't feel gangly or giraffe-like. She felt Mac was seeing her—the whole woman—and was loving her, even without touching her, just as she was.

**Dear Reader**

As summer gives way to autumn, this is a good time to reflect on how you feel about your loved ones. Being in love can be the most wonderful feeling on earth, yet why is it that so many people are frightened of expressing that love? That's certainly the case between our hero and heroine, yet, as in life, once expressed, it can lead to the greatest happiness. I think there's a lot to be learned in our books. Have fun learning...!

*The Editor*

**Anne McAllister** was born in California. She spent long lazy summers daydreaming on local beaches and studying surfers, swimmers and volleyball players in an effort to find the perfect hero. She finally did, not on the beach, but in a university library where she was working. She, her husband and their four children have since moved to the midwest. She taught, copy-edited, capped deodorant bottles, and ghostwrote sermons before turning to her first love, writing romance fiction.

# CATCH ME
# IF YOU CAN

BY
## ANNE McALLISTER

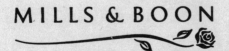

MILLS & BOON LIMITED
ETON HOUSE, 18-24 PARADISE ROAD
RICHMOND, SURREY TW9 1SR

For Tom, Julie and Allison
And for Donald and Christa

*First published in Great Britain 1993
by Mills & Boon Limited*

© Barbara Schenck 1993

*Australian copyright 1993
Philippine copyright 1993
This edition 1993*

ISBN 0 263 78262 X

*Set in Times Roman 10 on 11½ pt.
01-9310-50789 C*

*Made and printed in Great Britain*

# CHAPTER ONE

'THE important thing,' Emily said as she flung clothes into her duffel bag and scrabbled under the bed for her shoes, 'is not to panic.'

Her neighbour Gloria watched, leaning back against the headboard, sipping a soft drink complacently in the midst of the whirlwind. 'Right,' she drawled. 'You're right, of course.'

'I mean,' Emily went on, stuffing her feet into her espadrilles and zipping up the bag, 'given the commitments of the great Alejandro, chances are he won't even bother to look for us.'

'Of course,' Gloria said between sips.

Emily raked a comb distractedly through her long ash-blonde hair. 'But I'm not going to sit here in case he does. Not in Barcelona. It'd be different if we were in the States. That's my home base, not his. But here—oh, no. Alejandro Gomez probably knows every competent lawyer in Spain. He probably *owns* every competent lawyer in Spain. He'd have Tom away from me in a minute.'

Gloria wisely refrained from agreeing with that.

She only smiled sadly and sympathised with her friend's dilemma. They'd only known each other for the past year, ever since Emily had come to stay in her sister-in-law's apartment and met Gloria who lived downstairs. But, despite their relatively short acquaintance, they'd become close.

Gloria, an expatriate artist, had supported Emily through the months of her sister-in-law's illness and eventual death. She'd been there for Emily to lean on when she'd had no one else. She'd taken care of Emily's six-year-old nephew Tom after school while Emily had given language lessons, insisting that Emily needed to get out and do something other than hover around her nephew.

She'd even tried to get Emily to date, telling her that life had to go on. But, though Emily agreed with the sentiment, there were limits.

She didn't want to date. Not after her disastrous engagement to Marc.

Emily's fast-lane life as a top-flight Paris model had assured her the company of more men over the past five years than she'd believed possible when she'd been growing up in the American midwest.

At first, charmed by their interest, she'd taken them all at face value, naïvely believing they liked her as a person, not simply as a beautiful face.

'Such innocence. You have such innocence,' her friend, photographer Howell Evans, was always telling her. 'That's the beauty of you.'

But Emily didn't realise how innocent she really was until she met Marc Fontenot.

The handsome young car manufacturer had introduced himself at a Monte Carlo party, monopolised her evening, begun haunting her shows, her shoots, her life.

Everywhere she went, she'd found Marc already there, strong, virile, witty and enchanting, so cleverly charming that he swept her off her feet before she knew it. Worldly, debonair Marc was the antithesis of the men she'd grown up with. And Emily had been unsophisticated enough to think she'd charmed him, to think that he'd fallen in love with her just as she'd fallen in love with him.

When he'd asked her to marry him, she'd jumped to say yes.

If she hadn't overheard that phone call with his mistress the night before the wedding, she might have been married to him now. Thank heavens she had, picking up the phone and to hear him tell Lisette that he didn't really care about the woman he was to marry in what was to be one of Paris's most publicised weddings. 'Don't worry, *chérie*, you are my own true love,' he'd said softly. 'Emily, she is for show. Goes with the image. She looks good on paper, you know?'

Devastated, Emily hadn't waited around to discuss matters with him. Instead she'd run, making a thoughtless, panicky midnight dash to Howell's flat.

The paparazzi, expecting a sunny April wedding and getting instead a perplexed and furious jilted bridegroom, had had a field day with her defection.

But the one who had spotted her driving out of Paris in Howell's Jaguar had got the biggest scoop of all.

Grainy black and white photos and two-inch headlines proclaiming Emily's infidelity to Marc and Howell's to his famous reclusive sculptress wife had been everywhere before the week was out.

Emily had been frantic.

'Don't worry about it,' Howell, ever complacent, had told her.

But she had. She'd hated the notoriety, the falsehoods, the lunacy of it all. It was phony, foolish and wrongheaded, and she'd wanted to make it right again.

'I'll talk to the Press, tell them,' she'd said to Howell.

But he had simply laughed and shaken his head. 'The damage—what little there is—has already been done, Emily. You'll only make it worse by talking about it. Haven't you ever heard about women who protest too much?'

Emily had, but she was still uncomfortable with it. The curious looks, the snickers, the silences when she came into a room. It unnerved her.

Marielena's phone call, awful as it was, had come as a sort of salvation.

In nursing Mari and in caring for Tom, Emily had got her balance again. She realised how much she hated the crazy lifestyle she'd been living, how she wanted a plain, simple life.

She had been trying to get it in the months since Mari's death. She'd thought she'd been making progress for both herself and for Tom.

And now this!

'Ready?' Gloria asked now.

Emily glanced at her watch, bit her lip, then hefted her bag. She felt even more nervous than she was letting on. Cloak and dagger was not her style.

But ever since the head of Tom's school had told her of the letter they'd received from Alejandro Gomez, her late sister-in-law's high-powered brother, advising them to direct all bills and correspondence about Tom's education to him, she'd been worrying.

Marielena had never had anything to do with her family since she'd married Emily's brother, David, seven years before. The Gomezes hadn't approved. They hadn't come to the wedding. They hadn't been at Tom's baptism. They'd washed their hands of Marielena, and she of them. She hadn't even got back in touch with them after David died when his Navy plane went down in the Mediterranean three years before. Nor had she contacted them when she'd become ill.

'No,' she'd said adamantly when Emily had suggested calling them. 'They didn't want me when I married David. Now I don't want them!'

'But what about ... about Tom?'

'When I am gone, Tom will be yours. You love him.'

Emily did. More than anything or anyone in the world.

Tom was all the family she had. Her father had died when she was fifteen and her mother three years later. David had been her only sibling.

'You will do the best for him. I know that.' Mari's dark eyes had fixed on her confidently.

'Of course I will,' Emily had promised, but she'd heard plenty about the greedy, tough-minded patriarch of the Gomez family. 'But won't they try to take him away?'

Marielena's features had clouded. 'Never! They had their chance. They didn't want us when I was alive. They will not get Tom when I am dead.'

After the first couple of months, when no word had come from Mari's family, Emily had breathed more easily, thinking that all was well.

When she discovered, quite by accident, reading a business weekly over the shoulder of a fellow subway rider, that Alfredo Gomez y Ramirez had died of a heart attack only a few weeks after Mari's death, she had breathed more easily still. It was the father she'd feared. But now it appeared she had been wrong.

'Send the bills to him? Ridiculous. I'm Tom's guardian,' Emily had protested to the secretary at her nephew's school.

The woman had smiled indulgently. 'Ah, *sí, señorita*, of course you are. But Señor Gomez is a very important man. *Muy rico, no*?'

Very rich, yes. And very powerful—more so since his father's death. And suddenly obviously very interested in his nephew.

Emily shivered at the thought.

'He says his nephew is his responsibility,' the secretary went on.

Emily shook her head. 'He's mine.'

But she knew that her assertion wouldn't mean much if Gomez decided to press the issue. Alejandro Gomez had far more influence in Spain than she did.

'A Gomez can do anything he wants,' Mari had told her once.

'He couldn't stop you marrying David,' Emily had reminded her.

'Because I am a Gomez, too!'

Well, Emily wasn't a Gomez and didn't want to be. But if Alejandro Gomez thought he was going to take her nephew, he was wrong.

'I'm ready,' she said to Gloria. 'If Tom and I are going to be on that train, it's time to go.'

'Do you think Gomez is watching the building?' Gloria asked.

A week ago Emily would have laughed at the notion. But that was before Tom had said a strange man tried to talk to him on the playground, before a letter had come from Gomez's solicitor, before the great man himself had had his secretary call her on the phone.

'Señor Gomez will be pleased to take his nephew for the summer holidays,' she had told Emily in a haughty tone.

'Señor Gomez,' Emily had replied frostily, 'will please leave his nephew alone.'

There was a moment's silence on the other end of the line. Then the woman had said, 'Now see here, *señorita*. Señor Gomez is a very powerful man. You would do well to pay attention to him.'

'I don't have to pay attention to him,' Emily had said just as firmly.

'His nephew——'

'His nephew is also my nephew. And I have custody of him,' Emily retorted.

It was debatable which of them had hung up first.

Later that day there had been a ring at the doorbell for their apartment. 'I'll get it,' Tom had said, scrambling to his feet.

'No! I mean, I don't want you to answer it,' Emily had said, carefully modulating her voice, aware of the intensity of her first panicked reaction.

Tom looked puzzled. 'How come?'

'Salesmen,' Emily had fabricated. 'You know what pests they can be.'

Of course Tom didn't. And Emily had no idea if there were really door-to-door salesmen in Barcelona anyway. She just didn't want Tom answering the door. She had been all too sure who it would be.

'What if somebdoy else lets him in?'

A helpful neighbour, leaving the building, sometimes simply held the door open for whoever was ringing the bell.

'Then we just won't answer it up here,' Emily had said. 'But I doubt that will happen. See?' she'd said after a few moments' quiet. 'He's gone.'

But he hadn't, as the almost immediate pounding on the door so clearly proved.

'Wow,' Tom had breathed, his eyes round. 'I wonder what he's selling.'

Emily had grimaced. She'd tugged Tom into the kitchen. 'Come on. Let's get started on supper. He'll go away.'

But it had taken fifteen minutes of intermittent pounding before he did. And the event had left Emily shaking so much that as soon as she put Tom to bed that night she began to make plans.

She didn't want to disrupt Tom's school year, but it was almost over anyway. And one of the virtues of Mari's insistence on his attending one of the American schools in Barcelona was that it operated on the same schedule as American schools did. Consequently he'd only miss a few days if she took him out now in the middle of June.

And after the door-pounding incident, she had made up her mind to take him out. Not only out of school, but out of Spain.

However legal her guardianship might be, she had no faith in her ability to defend her right to her nephew in the face of the clout wielded by one of the most influential men in the whole country—a man who had family connections and business interests everywhere.

'Why not fly to the States right away?' Gloria wanted to know now.

'That's what he'd expect. He'd stop me for sure.'

'What if he finds out about this? What if he follows you?'

'I can fade into the woodwork as well as anyone.'

'With your face?'

'It's been a year since I was plastered on every subway wall in that perfume ad. And the photos from the fiasco with Marc were so bad no one would recognise me.'

Gloria didn't look convinced. She surveyed Emily's long ash-blonde hair and wide green eyes, her full lips and delicately moulded cheekbones. 'Even so...'

'Trust me.'

'Well...' Gloria brightened '...if you see him, you can run the other way.'

'I don't know what he looks like.'

Gloria was shocked. 'You haven't even seen a picture?'

'Marielena wouldn't have any in the house. ''They're dead to me,'' she used to say.'

'But a man so well-known, wouldn't he be in the magazines?'

'Not the great Alejandro. He keeps a very low profile. I've looked, believe me, but I've never found one. I've seen exactly one of his father—in the obituary. He had slick dark hair and a sinister moustache just like a bad guy in an old western.' Emily wrinkled her nose. 'No doubt the son is much the same.'

'Is he married?'

'I don't know. He wasn't the last I heard. Unlike Marc, he doesn't seem to go for articles or photos. Or publicity of any kind. Not of the personal variety in any case. I can find out anything I want to know about the companies the family owns, but nothing at all about the family itself.'

'Didn't Mari say anything?'

Emily shook her head. 'Never. It was as if they'd ceased to exist for her.'

'Maybe she didn't care.'

'I think she cared too much. I think their disapproval hurt her so much she just wouldn't talk about them at all.' Emily recalled the number of times she'd tried to bring up the topic of her sister-in-law's family, only to have Mari become agitated and change the subject. 'I can't believe that any family could be so cruel, but apparently they were.' She sighed and opened the front door. 'Come on. Let's get going.'

'Are you picking Tom up at school?'

'Bob Duggan's bringing him to the station.'

Gloria's brows lifted at that. 'I'll bet Bob was pleased.'

'He's a friend,' Emily said firmly.

Bob Duggan was the teacher at Tom's school whom she had gone around with now and then. Emily suspected he wanted rather more than that, but she didn't. And that was that, as far as she was concerned.

She hadn't wanted to drag him into this business with Gomez at all, knowing he might get the wrong idea, but she didn't have any other choice.

'Does Tom know about the trip?'

'I told him last night. Not why. Marielena never talked to him about her family, and I certainly didn't want to bring up anything that might make him think there was some big bad uncle who might snatch him away. He's had enough trauma for one little boy. I just said we were going on holiday.'

'So if not the States, where?'

Emily reached for her bag. 'Can't tell you. If you don't know, the big bad uncle won't be able to get it out of you.'

Gloria laughed. 'You're crazy. I hardly think he's going to torture me to find you.'

Emily hoped not. She hoped he'd forget the whole thing. In her more rational moments, she thought he might.

A man with multinational business interests like Alejandro Gomez would surely have plenty of more important things to keep him busy than a nephew he'd never seen. He might be interested right now, but if she could just get away and stay away for a few weeks she was fairly confident he'd forget all about her—and Tom.

'Here.' She handed the suitcase to Gloria. 'If he is lurking out there, I want him to think it's you going on the trip. I'm just coming down to see you off. Then we'll take separate taxis.'

Gloria looked impressed. 'Very clever.'

'Very desperate,' Emily corrected. She shut off the light, steered her friend out of the flat and didn't look back.

Gloria, with Emily's duffel, had already arrived at the train station by the time Emily did.

Emily found her at once. But in the bustle and rumble of thousands of travellers she began to fear that she and Bob might not even connect. He was the only one she'd confided her immediate destination to. And that was because it was the only way to ensure that they'd meet at the right train.

'Sure you don't want me to come with you?' Gloria asked as Emily took her duffel.

'Thanks, but I'll go on alone. Open any mail you think is important. Water the plants. I'll call when I can.'

She gave Gloria a quick hug, then walked away quickly towards the board with the departure schedule, found the destination she was looking for, descended the escalator, and almost sagged with relief to find Tom waiting with Bob at the bottom.

Bob hurried towards her. Tom was hopping from one foot to the other, a gleam of anticipation in his eye, a delighted grin on his face. It made her aware of how seldom she'd seen him smile since Mari's death, and how far she had to go to bring the happy-go-lucky nephew she remembered back to being himself again.

'This is it, Em. This is our train!' He was certainly eager enough right now.

She turned to Bob. 'Did you find the right car?'

'Right back there. Two seats reserved for Cerbère.' He reached for her, taking her arm possessively, and Emily wondered if she'd done the right thing in involving him.

She cleared her throat nervously. 'Is there anyone else in the compartment?'

'No. But there's one more seat reserved besides yours.'

Emily's fingers tightened around the handle of her bag and she looked around nervously. But besides a Pakistani family, a couple of harried-looking businessmen and an old lady with a shopping-bag, she didn't see anyone boarding the train.

'Do you think you were followed?' she asked Bob quietly, hoping that Tom, hunkered down and staring under the railway carriage, wouldn't hear.

'Not that I could see.' He smiled and touched her hair. 'You should have been a spy, Em. I think you're home free.'

She pulled away slightly, then sighed. 'I don't think I'll be home free until I get back to the States.'

'When will that be?'

She grimaced. 'When Uncle Dearest has lost interest. It won't take long—I hope.' Emily crossed her fingers.

'I'll be going back to Boston as soon as school is over. I can call you——'

She shook her head. 'I don't know where I'll be.'

'When you find out, call me.' He scribbled an address and thrust it at her. Emily took it and stuffed it in her bag. She wouldn't call. There was no reason for her to think that she could pursue a friendship with Bob when he had other ideas. It wouldn't be fair, and Emily really didn't want to lead him on.

He slipped an arm around her shoulders. 'Are you sure you have to do this?'

Emily looked down at Tom's dark head, at the sturdy body and small stubborn chin that so reminded her of David's. Her throat tightened whenever she contemplated the possibility that he might be taken from her, that she might never see him again. 'What else could I possibly do?' she asked with quiet anguish.

'You could marry me.'

She took an involuntary step backwards, her eyes widening.

Bob lifted his chin, looking defiant now. 'Why not? A single woman has far less chance of keeping custody than a married one.'

'I don't think——'

'You know I care for you.'

'Well, I——'

He raked a hand through his fair hair. 'I know we've never discussed marriage...'

They'd never even come close, Emily thought, staring at him as if he'd grown another head.

'But you must know how I feel. And, given the circumstances, you really ought to think about it.'

Emily felt her cheeks burn. Her mouth opened. 'Bob, I like you. Truly I do. But I don't think——'

'Don't think—yet.' He reached out a finger and gently closed her mouth. 'But keep it in the back of your mind, Emily, just in case.' He gave her a rueful look. 'I love you. And even if you don't feel the same way, you have to admit it could be a good idea—for Tom. And——' his mouth crooked into a hopeful grin '—I think you might learn to love me.'

Emily's fingers twisted together. Love? She wasn't even sure what the word meant. Not after Marc.

But she appreciated the gesture, even as she knew she couldn't take advantage of it.

She reached out and briefly touched his cheek, wanting to thank him and at the same time say she could never consider it. The thought of Alejandro Gomez stopped her.

What if he really did try to take Tom away from her?

Could she say outright that she would never consider marrying to keep custody of her nephew? In a normal, sane world, of course she never would marry a man she didn't love. But if it was the only way she could be sure to give Tom the life he deserved?

She dropped her hand. Her eyes mets Bob's. 'Thank you. You are very kind.'

'It's not kindness, Emily.'

Tom tugged her hand. 'Come on, Em. It's time.' He pointed to his watch importantly, then towed her towards the steps. 'See you, Mr Duggan.'

Bob's smile was wry. 'See you, Tom.' His gaze shifted to meet Emily's. 'I mean it,' he told her. 'I will see you. Even if you don't come back here.'

He leaned towards her, caught her in his arms and gave her a hug that was neither reassuring nor quick. Then he kissed her hard and stepped back. 'You don't have to think about marriage right now,' he said. 'You can, however, think about that.'

Emily, dazed from the ferocity of his kiss, stumbled up the steps into the car, mind reeling, lips trembling. 'A favour,' she muttered. 'I only wanted a favour.'

'Huh?' Tom peered up at her, confused.

'Nothing, dear.' She gave him a shaky grin, then peered at the seat reservations, then at the tickets stuck in the wall of the compartment.

'Here we are,' she said brightly even as she felt another twinge of apprehension seeing the third seat reservation tucked in the pocket. The way her life had been going lately...

She opened the door, half ready to bolt.

Sitting next to the window was a nun.

The sister, eighty if she was a day, nodded and patted the seat next to her, beckoning to Tom. She said something to him in Spanish which Emily, not yet fully fluent, wasn't able to catch. But Tom nodded happily and bounced on to the seat beside her, chattering in his mother's native tongue.

Emily wrestled their duffels on to the luggage rack overhead, all the while listening to him talk, catching the drift, aware that he was telling the sister that they were off on holiday, that he didn't have to go back to school at all until autumn, that he was going to have a super time. He sounded as cheerful as she'd heard him in months.

His mother's death had devastated him, even though she knew he had sensed it was inevitable. He had borne it stoically for the most part, only sobbing at night until Emily came to comfort him. Recently she thought he'd been sleeping much better, adjusting to life with her, to the family being just the two of them. She looked down at his dark head now, listened to his eager voice and ached with love for this small boy who had known so much loss in his life.

She was determined he wouldn't lose her as well.

Before she settled into the seat, she checked back out into the corridor. The only voices she heard were those of a pair of American school teachers discussing budgetary cutbacks and puffing cigarettes. Not a high-powered Spaniard in sight. For the first time in days Emily breathed more easily.

In a few short hours they would be in France. By morning they would arrive in Switzerland. Guido Farantino, another of her photographer friends, had a house there. She hadn't called to say she was coming. But he and Sophie, his wife, had given her a standing invitation. They wouldn't be expecting her to bring a child, but she knew he wouldn't care.

In any case, she didn't think she'd have to impose on them for long. Every day or so she'd check with Gloria to try to determine if Alejandro Gomez had given up looking for them.

Not *if*, she told herself. When.

He would. She was sure he would.

Pressing her lips together, crossing her fingers, she shut the door again and settled back into the seat next to Tom.

They had to change trains at Cerbère, leaving the RENFE coach train behind and heading towards Passport

Control before they could board the sleeper car that would take them through France during the night and deposit them bright and early the next morning in Geneva.

'We get to sleep on the train?' Tom was clearly delighted with the news. 'In beds?'

'Couchettes,' Emily told him. 'Bunk beds, really.'

'I always wanted bunk beds. And on a train! Where is it?' Tom was hopping up and down trying to catch a glimpse of the train.

'Through there.' Emily nodded towards the door through which they would pass after they got through Passport Control.

The door, to Tom, meant a train with bunks. To Emily, it meant freedom from the long arm of Alejandro Gomez.

Once through it she would be in France. Safe.

She glanced around nervously now, half expecting a huge, intimidating Alejandro Gomez to loom up out of nowhere and bar her way.

She and Tom were being jostled along in a multi-national sea of travellers, mostly university students, grubby and unshaven, but clearly having the time of their lives. Here and there she saw families, a few solitary travellers with packs on their backs, businessmen with black briefcases and tan raincoats.

''Sa matter?' Tom asked her.

'Nothing.' She gave him a bright smile, then glanced behind her again, one more time. For luck, she told herself.

And there he was!

She didn't need a picture. It was all too obvious. It could be no one else. Just descending the train, obviously in a hurry, pushing past people, a determined dark-haired man was striding in her direction.

He was a younger version of the picture she'd seen of Alfredo, right down to the slicked back hair and pencil-thin moustache.

Desperately she looked for an escape, stumbled into a couple carrying a baby and apologised in three languages.

'Are you OK?' Tom asked.

'F-fine. I——' She watched enviously as the man in the couple took the baby from his wife, then helped her adjust her pack. She wished she had someone to share her burden.

She wished fleetingly that Bob had come. If she had Bob along she might have had a chance. She supposed it was too much to hope that Gomez didn't know what she and Tom looked like. But if only for a moment he thought she was with Bob, thought she was married, that Tom was her child, it might give him pause to recon-sider; it might be enough.

And even though Bob wasn't here...

She grabbed Tom's hand and began to push forward again.

'Sorry,' she muttered, edging past a clutch of college students. 'So sorry. I'm...trying to catch up to my husband.'

She hoped God would forgive her the lie and that Tom wouldn't overhear her. '*Mi esposo está allá*,' she added and jerked her head towards the front of the line as she hurried on. 'Excuse me. *Discúlpeme, por favor. Discúlpeme. Pardon. Mon mari. J'ai besoin de...*I need...*Necesito a...mi esposo...*' She babbled in Italian as well. It didn't matter now.

They were within a few yards of the doorway. She saw the border guards flicking cursory glances at the pass-ports shoved at them, then waving people on.

'Please, let me by.' Emily cast another desperate glance behind her. He was coming around the corner of the last lane of travellers. Frantic, she shoved onwards, ignoring the mutters and grumbles. 'I just have to reach my husband! Please. I don't know where he's got to. I——'

She smacked against a hard masculine chest, looked up past a firmly chiselled jaw and high cheekbones into startlingly blue, stony cold eyes. Her fingers curled against his shirt-front.

Did she dare?

She wasn't even sure she articulated the thought. It was instinct. Panic. And really, what choice did she have with Gomez on her heels?

'Thank God, darling,' she babbled, throwing her arms around the stranger and hugging him hard. 'I thought I'd lost you!'

# CHAPTER TWO

EMILY tensed, expecting him to thrust her aside. The cold eyes flickered with surprise, then one dark brow arched and his mouth curved slightly at one corner.

'I hadn't known I was lost.'

Thank heavens he spoke English. She'd have been in hot water over her eyeballs if he hadn't. But the words were reassuringly familiar even though the accent was definitely British.

Grateful not to have been rejected out of hand, Emily clung. 'Er—well, you know how it is—how I am—about c-crowds and all. I didn't see you and——'

She had to stop babbling! The man would think she was a fool. She *was* a fool. But at least, she saw with a satisfied glance, Gomez appeared to be stopped in his tracks. He scowled at them.

Emily pressed closer, her lips against the stranger's shirt collar. 'I'm sorry. I just need a bit of help. It won't take long.'

She was startled to feel a hard arm come around her. 'This sort of help I can manage,' he said. And quite suddenly she felt his lips brush her cheek!

Emily jerked back, shivering at the unexpected touch of his mouth. Bob Duggan's kiss hadn't given her near the jolt this man's had.

'How's that?' he drawled. 'That help?'

'Er...' Emily managed. She swallowed, flicked another glance at Gomez. The stranger's gaze followed hers, then looked back at her assessingly.

'I'm not sure he's convinced,' he said, an unholy gleam in his eye. 'That wasn't much of a kiss.'

And before she could do a thing to stop him, he took another one!

Firm warm lips came down on hers, hard and insistent, demanding a response. And stunned, desperate, Emily gave him one.

Her eyes shut, and her lips parted, opening to him, just as if he were the man she'd been waiting for all her life.

She'd never kissed a man like that! Never even wanted to! Marc had always complained about her kisses. Icy Emily, he'd called her. He should see her now. She pushed back away from the stranger, frantic, amazed at the magnitude of her response.

'Relax.' Strong fingers kneaded the taut cords of her neck. He nodded in the direction of the man who'd been pursuing her. 'If you want to convince your friend, that is.'

Emily had forgotten about Gomez!

Now, heart hammering, fighting against the persuasiveness of his touch, she shot a desperate glance over her shoulder and was relieved to see that Gomez, though still staring at them, looked doubtful now, a deepening frown creasing his face.

Tom was staring up at Emily, his mouth open, his eyes agog. His gaze swivelled to the stranger. 'Who's he?'

'An...old friend,' Emily said quickly. She shoved Tom ahead of her, gave her rescuer a brief grateful smile and edged forward, still shaken.

The stranger stayed right behind her. Emily could feel his hand against her back, steering her along just as if he really were her husband. She trembled slightly. Nerves, she told herself. Only nerves.

'Irate boyfriend?' the stranger murmured in her ear.

'Of course not.'

'Don't tell me he caught you with his wife.'

Emily gasped.

He gave her a sardonic grin and a negligent shrug. 'You never know.'

She glared at him. Those maddening fingers came up again to caress the back of her neck.

'Relax, sweetheart. I'll take care of you.'

'I don't need you to take care of me,' Emily said stiffly.

'No? Forgive me if I find that a little hard to believe.'

'I just need to get across the border.'

'Why?'

'It's a long story.' And, thank heavens, before she had time to say more than that, they had passed by the guards and were out the other side, hurrying along the corridors, and heading towards the stairs to the platform where they would board the train to Geneva. She almost fainted with relief.

The stranger shored her up.

She pulled away. 'Let me go. I'm fine.'

'Of course you are.' He held up her hand so they could both see it trembling. Emily grimaced.

'So, why don't you just tell me? What are you running away from?'

If he'd sounded the least bit sympathetic, Emily might have told him. If the truth were known, she would have liked nothing better than to throw herself on him and let him solve her problems. But he stood there so judgementally, as if this were all her fault.

'It's not important.'

'You were scared to death.'

'I was not! I was just...just...trying to get away from a persistent jerk.'

It wasn't precisely a lie. It was just a matter of interpretation. Gomez was a persistent jerk, and if he wasn't after her but after Tom, well, that wasn't the stranger's business.

While Tom went on ahead, she stopped at the foot of the stairs and turned back, lifting her gaze to meet the stranger's. His eyes were the most beautiful she'd ever seen. They were also the coldest. Even colder, she thought, than those of the nasty Señor Gomez. 'Look,' she said, 'I've already said I'm sorry. I...I shouldn't have involved you. But it's over now. I appreciate your assistance, and now I'll be on my way. Thank you.' She started past him, but he caught her arm.

'Hold on.'

'What?' Emily demanded.

'You don't think you owe me?'

'I've said thank you.'

'That's nice. It's not quite what I had in mind.'

And before she could do more than blink, he had his arms around her and was kissing her again.

This kiss was hotter and hungrier than the last, as if her earlier response, eager though it had been, hadn't satisfied. His lips tasted, tormented. His tongue teased, cajoled. And Emily, desperate, fought him—and her own traitorous desires—every step of the way.

Finally she could do nothing else.

'Damn!' He pulled back, wiping a hand across his mouth. 'You bit me, you little termagant.'

'Damned right I did! Persistent jerks seem to abound hereabouts!' Emily countered roundly, infuriated. And turning on her heel, she stamped up the steps.

She didn't look back to see where he went. She didn't want to know. How on earth did she pick them? First Marc, then this...this insufferable creep. Just because she had needed a bit of help...!

She wiped a hand across her mouth, trying to rid herself of the taste, the memory of him.

Damn him!

She tried not to think about him. He didn't matter. What mattered was that she and Tom were free. Thanks to the obnoxious stranger, they had made it to France unimpeded. It would be a great deal harder for Alejandro Gomez to take Tom away from her outside of Spain.

At least now they had some breathing-space. The overnight train to Geneva would give them even more.

'He must be a very good friend.' Tom was looking up at her curiously.

Emily looked down, startled. 'What?'

'You didn't seem to mind kissing him.'

She felt hot blood in her cheeks. 'I . . . told you, he's an old friend.'

Tom shrugged. 'OK. I found our car.' He pointed to the one just beyond the head of the stairs. 'That's the right number, isn't it?'

Emily nodded. 'You're really sharp.'

Tom beamed, then surveyed the length of the train. 'It's a long 'un. Can we walk to the end of it? Please? Can we?'

Emily wanted to say no. She wanted to tuck him safely away in their compartment and bolt the door until they were on their way. She wanted to sit down before she fell down. The stranger's kiss was still making her tremble. But Tom was so eager and he'd been so good.

'All right. But let's hurry. The train leaves in ten minutes and we still have to find our compartment.'

'I can find it easy,' Tom said confidently, setting off at a run towards the end of the train.

'Aren't you just a little tired?' Emily asked when, at the end, she finally caught up with him.

'Sorta. But we get to sleep on the train.' Tom gave a happy skip. 'That'll be super, won't it?'

'Yes.' Emily needed a good night's sleep.

She made a lousy fugitive. She'd been running for scarcely more than three hours and already she felt as if she'd been on the road for years. She glanced at her watch. 'We've got only a couple of minutes.'

They were back with a minute to spare.

Tom took the reservation slip, flashed her a grin and pounded up the steep steps ahead of her. When she finally got up the steps and turned the corner, he was walking down the narrow corridor, standing on tiptoe outside every compartment, checking the numbers.

'*Aquí está*. Here it is!'

Emily compared the number on the reservation slip with the number on the compartment, then nodded. 'You're right.'

The train lurched and began to move.

Emily opened the door.

'You!'

There on the bottom bunk, his tie undone, his shirt unbuttoned, sat the infuriating stranger!

He gave her a typically infuriating grin and made a mocking little bow. 'We have to stop meeting like this.'

Furious, Emily averted her gaze, not wanting to see the wicked gleam in his eyes nor the visible expanse of hair-roughened chest. But dropping her gaze didn't help, for when she did she noticed that his trouser button was undone. 'What are you...? You can't be here! You're in the wrong compartment!'

'No.'

'This is our compartment!' She waved the reservation slip in his face.

He took it out of her hand, scanning it, then shrugging. 'So it is.' He smiled again. 'Good thing we're married, isn't it?'

Emily started to splutter.

Tom giggled. 'He's teasing you,' he told Emily matter-of-factly, making her feel even more of a fool. He looked at the man. 'Aren't you?' he asked.

The man regarded Tom solemnly for a moment, then reached out and tousled Tom's dark hair. 'Of course.'

He turned to Emily. 'Even though I was here first, I'll be generous. You two can have whichever berths you want. I'll take what's left.'

'You'll do no such thing! This is *our* compartment.'

'And mine, too,' he said simply and proffered a reservation slip of his own.

'There's been a mistake. There has to be! They wouldn't put you in with us! You'll have to find somewhere else.'

'Have you ever tried finding a berth on a sleeper in the middle of summer without a reservation?'

'No, but——'

'Can't be done. Rarer than hen's teeth.'

'Nonsense,' Emily said briskly. 'There's an extra one right here.'

'Only because my... travelling companion couldn't make it.'

It didn't take Emily much imagination to conjure up what sort of travelling companion hadn't been able to come along. She scowled.

The train was picking up speed even as they spoke.

'How unfortunate for you,' she said icily.

'In the circumstances, it's probably just as well.' He gave her a cool smile.

Emily bristled, catching his insinuation with no trouble at all. 'Don't expect me to take her place!'

'Oh, I don't think you'd mind all that much.'

'Go to hell,' Emily muttered, and was even more furious with him when her words caused Tom to look at her, shocked.

'Sorry,' she muttered. Here she was supposed to be feeling safe now that they were in France, and instead she felt as if her life was slipping totally out of control. 'There must be a berth somewhere that you can use.'

'You're welcome to try to find one.'

'Fine.' She took Tom by the hand. 'Come on.'

But Tom, for the first time that night, dug in his heels. 'I want to stay here.'

'Tom.' Emily pulled him towards the door.

'Let him stay,' the man suggested. 'He's probably exhausted, poor kid.'

'He's——'

'I'm tired,' Tom said as if on cue.

'You're fine. I don't——'

'What's the matter?' the man challenged. 'Do you think I'll steal him?'

'I don't think *you'll* steal him,' Emily said sharply, and regretted her emphasis the moment the words were out of her mouth.

Tom looked instantly worried. Emily shut her eyes and tried to regain control. 'Nobody's going to steal you,' she said to Tom, then raked a hand through her hair. 'Nobody's going to steal him,' she repeated firmly for the benefit of the interloper. 'But he's coming with me.'

'But——' Tom protested.

'Now.'

He continued to look mulish, but Emily wasn't budging. She jerked open the door.

'Never mind. I'll look,' the stranger said gruffly. 'You wait here.'

'Thank you.'

He gave her a grim smile. 'Do you mind if I leave my bags here while I'm gone?'

She shook her head. 'Please do.'

'Thank you very much.' There was irony in his tone, too, but she was too tired to care.

'I thought you said he was your friend?' Tom pointed out as soon as the man had left. 'You kissed him.'

'Yes, well, that doesn't mean we're going to sleep with him. He shouldn't be sharing our compartment.'

'But it's his, too,' Tom protested.

'Not for long, I hope. Come on. Let's get you into your pyjamas and you can go to bed.'

Tom, having admitted to being tired and fascinated with the idea of actually sleeping on the train, didn't argue. He changed quickly. Then, while he went to brush his teeth, Emily took advantage of his absence to get ready for bed herself.

Wearily she stripped off her dress and bra, opened her duffel, then pulled out the elongated T-shirt she intended to sleep in.

It was over her head when the door opened. 'Back already?' she asked through the folds of cotton. 'That was fast.'

'I'd have been quicker if I'd known what was waiting.' The voice was an octave deeper than Tom's.

Emily yanked the T-shirt all the way on and glared into the stranger's eyes. Her face flamed. 'You could have knocked.'

'And miss the floor show? No way. Besides, I should think you'd be used to it. I'm surprised you care.'

'Why shouldn't I care? A man I don't even know walks in when I'm barely dressed, and I'm not supposed to care?'

'You don't care when you model, do you?'

She stiffened. 'How do you know I model?'

'I've seen your... face.' The way his eyes travelled the length of her body and the discreet pause in his words let her know that wasn't all he'd seen. Damn him. Was she really that recognisable? That memorable?

'That's different,' she said shortly. 'Besides, I don't model any more.'

He cocked his head. 'No? Why not?'

She folded her clothes and put them into her bag, keeping her back to him. 'I have other priorities. Not that it's any of your business.'

'Tom?'

She spun around. 'How did you know his name?'

'You called him by it.' His tone was patient. The look in his eyes was not.

She felt suddenly foolish. 'Oh, yes. Of course.'

'But surely you had him while you were still modelling?'

'He's...not my son. He's my nephew. I'm his guardian.' She didn't want to explain any more. She reached for his suitcases. 'Here. You'll be wanting these.'

He took them and stowed them underneath the berth.

'What are you doing?' Emily demanded.

'Couldn't find room at the inn. I told you I wouldn't be able to.'

'I'll bet you didn't even look.'

He opened the door. 'Look yourself, then, sweetheart.'

She was about to. But just then Tom came back, and behind him she saw Gomez—coming down the corridor. The colour drained from her face.

She yanked Tom in and shut the door at once, twisting the lock and putting her back against it.

'Another persistent jerk?' The stranger mocked her. Emily glared.

Tom looked up at him quizzically. 'Are you staying?'

The man looked at Emily, a sardonic smile twisting his mouth. He waited.

Emily met his gaze, then let hers slide away. She drew a breath. 'He's staying,' she said.

'Imagine that,' the man murmured.

Gritting her teeth, Emily ignored him. She bustled about in the cramped space, boosting Tom up to tuck him into the upper berth he had chosen. Then, turning her back to their new compartment mate, she slipped quickly into her own below.

For a long moment he just stood there. Resolutely Emily faced the wall, holding her breath. If he reached for her, touched her, she'd scream.

He reached over and flicked out the light.

Emily lay in the darkness that was supposed to be her refuge and knew for a fact that it was not.

There was nothing remotely comforting about hearing the clink of his belt buckle, the rasp of his zip, the soft sounds of him fumbling with his buttons, unlacing his shoes.

'You don't have to get undressed,' she hissed at him.

'You want to do it for me?'

She gave an irritated wuffle. He laughed.

He was so close she could feel the heat from his body as he moved in the tiny space. Her fingers tightened on the sheet. Then his trousers hit the floor, the berth right opposite creaked and he slipped beneath the blanket.

'You know,' he said conversationally, 'I've never slept with someone to whom I've never been properly introduced.'

'You're not sleeping with me!'

'Close. But not close enough.'

'Far too close,' Emily gritted.

'Do you think so?' His voice was softly mocking. 'We'll see.' He was silent for a moment, then said, 'So, what's your name, pretty lady?'

She debated lying to him, then decided not to bother. 'Emily Musgrave, not that it makes a bit of difference.'

'Oh, it does,' he said. 'A world of difference. Pleased to meet you, Emily Musgrave.' He paused, then added, 'After all this time.'

Emily frowned. 'All what time?'

'Why, all the time I've seen you staring at me from magazines and such.'

'That's not me,' she muttered.

'Really?' He didn't sound as if he believed her. He rolled over on to his side so that he faced her. She refused to look at him, stared instead up at the dark form of the berth above her head.

'Who are you, then?' he asked her.

'Never mind. It's not important.'

'I think it is,' he said. His voice was silky. 'And if you won't tell me, I guess I'll just have to find out.'

She heard both seduction and threat in his words. Or thought she did. Heavens, she was confused tonight.

'Who are you?' she asked grudgingly after a moment. She didn't really want to know, didn't want to pursue the acquaintance any further than it had already gone, which was much too far. But she needed a name, some way to pigeonhole him, control the effect he had on her.

'MacPherson,' he said. 'Sandy MacPherson. You can call me Mac,' he added softly. 'All my wives do.'

It was not the getaway Emily had planned.

MacPherson rolled over in his berth and, seconds later, was snoring, while for hours Emily lay stiff and unmoving in hers, feeling with her whole body the whoosh and thrum of the train as it sped through tunnel and countryside, aware with her whole mind of the man lying just inches away from her.

Sandy MacPherson. Mac.

No, her mind instantly corrected. *Mr* MacPherson.

Even if 'all his wives' did call him Mac, she certainly wasn't going to!

Was he married?

Somehow she doubted it. Though he was certainly sexy and attractive enough to have had his fair share of women dangling after him, there was nothing domesticated about Sandy MacPherson.

Sandy didn't fit him. It made him sound gentle, domestic, like a tabby cat perhaps. But there was nothing tabbylike about him. He was far more the dangerous jungle cat, hungry and on the prowl. She didn't think there was much chance that he went docilely home to one particular hearthside every night.

She had really done it when she'd latched on to him. It had been sheer stupidity to do so. Look where it had got her! Out of the frying-pan into the fire.

She had enough on her plate right now, trying to take care of Tom and avoid Gomez, without having a man like MacPherson around to complicate things.

And she had no doubt that he intended to complicate them. That mocking grin and those hard blue eyes told her quite clearly that he thought she was ripe for the picking. She knew that her modelling career made her seem fair game to lots of men. She must be fast and loose if she let her body be photographed and displayed for the world—that was what most people seemed to think.

Certainly that was what Marc had thought.

He'd been amazed at first by her scrupulously proper behaviour. But it hadn't put him off, so she'd thought he must be pleased. She hadn't realised he was busy getting his loving elsewhere.

She didn't make the mistake of thinking that MacPherson was pleased by her behaviour. It must annoy him a great deal, especially when she'd flung her arms around him in the first place. Some men might have called it provocative, might have accused her of leading them on. Men expected sex as payment for everything, she thought irritably.

'Tough,' she muttered, even though she felt faintly guilty for her actions. She owed him a thank-you, nothing more.

She punched her pillow and tried to go to sleep. She didn't have a prayer.

It was because of Gomez, she told herself. It was because she wasn't cut out to be a fugitive, because she was worried about Tom, because she was scared.

But it wasn't Gomez she was thinking about. Or Tom.

And if she was scared it had nothing to do with either of them. It had entirely to do with the man in the bunk next to hers—and with the way she'd reacted to him.

Carefully, quietly, she rolled on to her back, then turned her head just enough so that she could glimpse his profile in the darkness. He had shifted over on to his side, so all she could really see was a large lump just opposite. It didn't matter. She didn't need light to remember the way he looked—nor the way he'd looked at her when he'd come in and found her half dressed. There had been hunger in his gaze. And disdain. There had been curiosity. And desire. His eyes had made her shiver with their intensity and their coldness. And yet, once or twice, for a fleeting instant, she'd thought she'd glimpsed a flame.

She remembered the way they had skated over her, tracing the tilt of her chin, the lift of her breasts, the curve of her hips.

The world had seen more of her in swimsuit ads than MacPherson had. Yet never had she felt so exposed.

Damn the man.

Damn all men, for that matter, Emily thought irritably. Sandy MacPherson, Bob Duggan and, most especially, that miserable rotten Alejandro Gomez, who was making all this necessary.

Sleep, she counselled herself. Sleep and forget them.

She sighed, rolled over and punched her pillow. The train whooshed into another tunnel, rattling the windows and making her ears pop. Tom whimpered softly in his sleep. MacPherson snored.

It was going to be a very long night.

It wasn't yet light when the train stopped in Lyons, but Emily was awake. Again. Or, perhaps, still.

Whoever said that the soft sway and lulling clickety-clack of night-time train travel were instant sleep-inducers obviously hadn't experienced what she had. Or maybe his compartment had been air-conditioned and his sleeping companions less noisy. Or maybe he hadn't been worried that the shadow passing the door every so often was Alejandro Gomez.

Probably, she thought in retrospect, it had been a mistake to open the door and peek out the first time she'd seen the shadow. If she hadn't, she never would have seen his back disappearing into the compartment four doors down. She might not have sat huddled and fretting for the better part of the night, until MacPherson's gruff, 'For heaven's sake, go to sleep,' sent her skittering under the blanket.

He'd rolled over and glared at her. 'Stop worrying. I'll protect you, pretty lady.'

But Emily didn't think she believed that. Oh, he might protect her from Gomez, all right. But who was going to protect her from him?

Now she stared out at Lyons's mostly deserted Part-Dieu station and wondered if she ought to wake Tom and get off. If she did, would she be home free?

Possibly. At least as far as MacPherson went. But there were drawbacks, too.

She didn't know a soul in Lyons. She'd have to check into a hotel, and there she'd be far easier to find than if she were able to stay with friends. If she could get to Guido's, it would be much better. But could she get to Guido's?

She probably could if she stayed with MacPherson. Gomez hadn't seized her in Cerbère, she suspected, because she'd clung so tightly to MacPherson and if he'd tried to interfere there would have been a scene.

Gomezes, she gathered, didn't like scenes. They were the bastions of propriety, according to her sister-in-law. Proper, dignified, never willing to air their grievances in public. They just made you miserable in private, she thought grimly.

'Now what?'

Emily started, then turned to find MacPherson raised up on one elbow, scowling at her.

It was still scarcely light and she couldn't make out his features well, only the rumpled state of his dark hair and the shadowy darkness along his jaw. He looked more predatory than ever. She tucked the blanket more closely around her. 'Nothing. I don't sleep well on trains.'

'Nor do I.'

'That wasn't you I heard snoring?' she said tartly.

A grin flashed in the darkness. 'I was faking.' He sat up and the blanket fell away. She saw that he was bare-chested, experienced the same sudden shortness of breath she'd felt last night, and hastily averted her eyes. She expected him to remark on her prudishness and was relieved when he didn't.

'You're getting off in Geneva?'

'I might get off here.'

'That's a stupid idea.'

She bristled. 'What do you know about it?'

'I know you're running.'

'I'm not——'

'And if you're running, you need a plan,' he went on, just as if she hadn't spoken. 'You can't just dash around willy-nilly dragging the boy with you.' He sounded calm, matter-of-fact, as if runaway females were not all that unusual in his life.

Perhaps, Emily thought grimly, they weren't.

'So what do you suggest?' she asked gruffly.

'That you stop springing up like a jack-in-the-box every time you see that dark-haired fellow. It's making me dizzy and it's not doing you a damned bit of good. If you need to get away from him, you have to stop calling attention to yourself.'

'You know a lot about that, do you?' Emily asked sourly.

'A fair bit.'

'You plan lots of escapes?'

He smiled. 'Some.'

'Member of British Intelligence, I suppose?' she sniffed.

He shook his head. 'A writer.'

She stared. He looked as much like her idea of a writer as she resembled a frumpy *hausfrau*. Writers wore tweedy jackets with leather elbow patches. They smoked pipes and had bald patches.

'What do you write? Men's erotic fantasies? Chance encounters in the railway station?'

'There's an idea!' He leered. 'Want to try a little research?'

Emily, wishing she'd kept her mouth shut, held the blanket close against her breasts. 'Very funny.'

'I doubt it would be funny at all.' His tone shifted and there was a soft seductiveness in it now that made Emily both aware and anxious at the same time. 'I think it would be marvellous.'

'Stop it,' she muttered.

His grin vanished and he gave her a long, assessing look. 'You're an odd duck, you know that,' he said almost conversationally. 'Most models don't blush and go all frantic when a man looks at them.'

Emily scowled. 'You know all about models, too, do you?'

'I've dated a few.'

She didn't doubt it. Most of the ones she knew would have jumped at a chance to date a man as dishy as this one. 'For research purposes?' she asked tartly.

'No.' He grinned wickedly. 'But I've probably used a bit of the material unintentionally.'

'And you'll use this, too, I suppose.'

'Nothing's happened. Yet.'

'Nothing's going to happen!'

'Then you don't have anything to worry about, do you?'

The train began to move again. Emily sighed and looked away at the station as they picked up speed and moved away. 'Much you know,' she muttered.

MacPherson leaned forward, wrapping his arms around his knees. Emily could feel his gaze on her and she deliberately looked away.

'What's this guy got on you, Emily Musgrave?'

She didn't answer.

'It's more than just unrequited love, isn't it?'

She hunched her shoulders. 'Why? Do you want to use it in a book?'

'I never use real people. The places are real. The details are. The stories are pure imagination.'

'Then why?'

He shrugged. 'I thought maybe I could help you plan.'

She examined his words for undercurrents and was surprised not to find any. He hadn't been exactly a knight in shining armour so far. Still, he didn't seem wholly willing to pitch her into the arms of her adversary. Maybe if she could...

'No.' It was too tempting. It would be too easy. Tom was her responsibility, no one else's. Besides, her reactions to MacPherson were far too volatile. 'You've helped enough, thanks.' She turned her head and stared out of the window again, afraid of saying more.

They were heading out of the city now, big buildings and apartment houses giving way to small family dwellings.

'I have,' he agreed after a moment. 'So you owe me.'

Emily's gaze snapped back to meet his. 'Not another kiss!'

He grinned. 'I thought it wasn't bad at all, myself, but if you'd rather, I'll settle for something else this time.'

'What?'

'An explanation.'

She knew he wouldn't leave off, retire gracefully, admit defeat. His kind never did. She sighed. 'I... have something he wants.'

'Tom.'

She gave a little jerk. 'How do you know?'

'What else? You aren't wearing the Crown Jewels, and you're far too skittish to be running drugs. You'd be picked up in a minute. So, who is he?'

Emily looked out of the window. 'My sister-in-law's brother. I think.'

'You don't know?' He sounded incredulous.

'I've never met him,' Emily admitted. 'I suppose it could be one of his henchmen,' she added defensively. 'But something tells me it's Gomez in the flesh. Goosebumps or something. I think I get them whenever he's close.' Emily tried to smile, but it wasn't funny. Nothing about Alejandro Gomez was funny.

'And he wants Tom?'

'Yes.'

MacPherson shifted and leaned against the wall of the compartment. 'If you're his guardian, what's the problem?'

'It won't stop him.'

MacPherson lifted a sardonic brow. 'Who is he? A Mafia don?'

'Might as well be. His name is Alejandro Gomez. He and his family practically own half the business interests in Madrid. They have company branches in every major city in Spain. They have corporate offices in London and Paris, Rio and Singapore. I think they own the world.'

MacPherson laughed. 'I think you exaggerate.'

'Maybe. But suffice it to say they have a damned sight more influence than I do. Particularly in Spain.'

'But if your guardianship is legal...? Or have you perhaps given him reason to contest it? Maybe you've led a less than pure life, Emily Musgrave?' The insinuation in his voice infuriated her.

'I have not!' Emily could scarcely keep her voice down.

'Right,' he drawled. 'You do resemble purity personified.'

'Think whatever you like,' she said stiffly, 'it won't change what I am.'

'I never imagined it would,' he said easily. 'So if you're pure and blameless, what chance has he got?'

'Less now that I'm in France,' she admitted. 'But he's still here. I thought he'd leave. The fact that he hasn't worries me. He might try something. Might...try to take Tom away physically.'

'You're sure he wants to take him away from you?'

'What else would he want?'

MacPherson shrugged. 'Visiting rights?'

Emily snorted. 'He never wanted them before. It isn't as if he cared about Tom before Mari died. That's my sister-in-law,' she explained, and he nodded curtly.

'When did she die?'

'About five months ago.'

'Of what?'

'She had a rare blood disease. When she knew there was no hope for recovery, she asked me to come and take care of her and Tom.'

'And you just dropped everything and came?' She could hear the scepticism in his voice.

'Yes. It—it was a good time for me to get away,' she added honestly.

A corner of his mouth lifted in a smile that wasn't precisely pleasant. 'Right. You were jilting somebody about that time, weren't you?'

She stared. 'How did you——?'

'I read the papers. Like everyone else.'

'I broke off my engagement.'

'Left him at the altar.'

'You don't know everything.'

'Enough. You are a relatively famous lady. Or should I say, infamous?'

'Don't say anything!' She scowled at him, then drew her knees up to her chest and hugged them tightly. Roll on Geneva, she thought.

'So go on,' MacPherson said after a moment. 'You selflessly went to nurse your sister-in-law——'

'I did the best I could,' she said sharply. 'I loved her. I love Tom. That's why she left him to me. She wanted Tom to be raised by the person who loved him most!'

'What happened to Tom's father?'

'David was a Navy pilot. He died three years ago in a crash.'

MacPherson frowned. She couldn't tell what he was thinking. He had one of those enigmatic faces, determinedly indecipherable. 'It must have been rough for the boy,' he said after a moment. 'That's a lot to lose in such a short life.'

'Yes. That's another reason I'm not letting anyone take him from me. He's just getting adjusted again after his mother's death. Can you imagine what it would be like for him to be yanked away from me and given to people he's never seen before?'

'Why hasn't he?'

'Because as far as the Gomezes were concerned, he didn't exist.'

She saw MacPherson's jaw tighten and went on to explain, 'They didn't approve of David and Marielena getting married, didn't think he was good enough for her. The Gomezes are very conscious of their lineage. An American simply wasn't good enough for them! They're not pure Spanish themselves. But the part that isn't, according to Marielena, is some sort of English or French nobility.' Emily's mouth twisted bitterly. 'If you can't marry a duke, don't marry at all, seems to be that family motto.'

'Interesting philosophy.'

Emily snorted. 'Stupid, if you ask me. They never even wanted to meet David. Just told Marielena that if she married him she might as well be dead as far as they were concerned. And they meant it. She never heard from them again.' Her fingers clenched on the blanket and she stared unseeing out of the window.

The countryside was bathed now in the soft glow of early morning light. Snowcapped peaks loomed in the distance.

'But when she really did die, suddenly everything changed,' she went on hoarsely. 'They found out about Tom and wanted him. They tried to take over. Wanted his school bills sent to them. Wanted his reports. Sent people to the school to try to talk to him. Came by our flat.'

'Then why haven't you met him?'

'I told you! I wasn't letting him near Tom. I don't trust him. In Spain, what Alejandro Gomez wants, Alejandro Gomez gets.'

'But not in Geneva?'

Emily's chin jutted. Her fists clenched. She met MacPherson's gaze firmly and squarely. 'Not in Geneva. Or anywhere else.'

# CHAPTER THREE

IF ONLY it were that simple.

But an hour later, when Emily gathered up Tom and the bags and bade a brief, somewhat stiff farewell to Sandy MacPherson at the door of the train and hurried along the platform towards Customs, she knew it would not be.

There, just beyond the Customs men, already leaning against a wall and scanning the crowds that passed, exactly as she had feared, stood Alejandro Gomez.

Emily pulled up short, looking desperately for another way out.

There wasn't one.

Oh, help, Emily thought and, just as she did so, heard behind her an all too familiar voice. 'Lost me again, did you?'

Tom turned. 'Hi, Mac! Are you coming with us?'

MacPherson looked at Emily. Slowly his gaze travelled past her towards the man leaning against the wall, then just as slowly it moved lazily back to focus on her again. 'I don't know. Am I?'

Emily's own gaze went to the heavens. But all the divine intervention it appeared she was going to get was standing right smack in front of her, his blue eyes challenging her.

She had no desire to tangle with him. All she could hope was that Gomez had none either. She drew a deep breath, then gave him her sunniest smile. 'I believe you are.'

His own smile was knowing as he reached for her bag and took her arm with his.

She saw Gomez frown and start forward. MacPherson's jaw tightened and the hard blue eyes focused right on Gomez for an instant, seeming almost to dare him to interfere.

To Emily's giddy relief, the other man looked away first. She breathed a sigh of relief.

They got through Customs without a hitch, MacPherson playing his part to the hilt. His hand slipped away from her arm to rest against the small of her back, his face was so close to hers that his breath fanned her ear.

Emily's pulses raced. From the close encounter with Gomez, she assured herself. Certainly not from MacPherson's close proximity.

But she was glad when they finally rounded the corner, merged into the morning rush-hour crowd of pedestrians, and the dark-haired man disappeared from view so that she could pull away and breathe more easily.

'Where to?' MacPherson asked her.

'Taxi. But you needn't come with us.' She might as well have saved her breath.

'Where are you going?'

'A friend of mine—a photographer—lives here.'

'Evans?'

Emily looked at him, surprised at the harshness of his tone. 'Howell? Do you know him?'

'Of him.' Whatever he knew, it didn't sound as if he liked it.

'Howell lives in Wales,' Emily said. 'This is Guido Farantino. Do you know him?'

'No.' He was scowling now as they shoved through the crowd. Emily could still feel his hand, hard and warm, against her back.

It was disconcerting how strongly she reacted to his touch. When Bob Duggan touched her, she felt nothing. When most men touched her she felt nothing. The last person who had made her tingle with awareness had been Marc.

And she would do well to remember that, she thought grimly.

At least when they got to the taxi queue, he'd go his own way. 'Wonderful,' she said when they arrived. 'We've made it. Thank you very much.'

'You're quite welcome,' MacPherson said, but his hand stayed right where it was.

'You needn't hang around, Mr MacPherson.'

He was still scowling. 'I told you, my name is Mac. And I'm not "hanging around", sweetheart. I'm waiting for a taxi.'

She felt hot blood rise in her cheeks. 'Of course.' Her fingers twisted on the strap of her bag. Idiot, she chastised herself.

Fortunately the line moved quickly and before long the next taxi was theirs. Or would have been if MacPherson hadn't climbed in after them!

Emily stopped. 'What the——?'

He shoved her in. 'Get going.'

'But——'

'You have company,' MacPherson said, jerking his head towards the back of the queue. 'Or maybe you don't care.'

Emily glanced towards the rear of the line, knowing whom she would see, and not surprised to find him there. Her moustachioed nemesis was staring right at her. She started to tremble.

'Who's following us?' Tom wanted to know, scrambling up on to his knees and peering around curiously.

'Never mind, Tom,' Emily said. The last thing she wanted was him worrying.

But Tom was not deterred. 'That guy?' The boy pointed at Gomez. 'I've seen him before.'

Emily sighed. 'At Cerbère last night.'

'Before that. At school.'

Emily's teeth clenched. So she'd been right. Gomez had been trying to infiltrate Tom's life for weeks now.

MacPherson's fingers came up to massage the taut cords of her neck. 'Probably just someone who looks like him,' he said to Tom, and to Emily, 'Calm down. Think about something else.'

Emily glared at him. 'What?'

'This.' And before she could move, his lips touched hers. It was a very persuasive kiss. It spoke of hunger and desire and need. It reminded her of all the feelings he'd excited in her last night, feelings she'd been trying to assure herself were nothing more than the product of tension and stress and an over-stimulated imagination.

It gave Emily far more to think about than she'd ever wanted! Her mind reeled.

The driver slipped into the front seat. '*Où allez-vous?*'

MacPherson lifted his head and looked at her expectantly.

Emily stared back, unseeing. She knew what he was asking, she just couldn't form the words.

'The address?' Mac coaxed.

Face flaming, she dug through her purse and found Guido's address, then handed it to the driver, who looked at it, nodded and pulled away from the kerb.

'That's better,' MacPherson breathed into her ear.

Emily wasn't sure about that.

The streets, clogged with morning traffic and road-repair crews, made their progress slow. But gradually they skirted Lake Geneva, heading out into the residential area.

Emily didn't know how far it was to Guido's house, but they couldn't get there quickly enough as far as she was concerned. It wasn't only going to be her haven in which to hide from Gomez. She needed to get away from MacPherson!

He was the wrong man in the wrong place at the wrong time.

There was nothing right about him at all.

Except the way he kissed.

It would be a good thing when she got to Guido's and could say goodbye to Mr Sandy MacPherson. He was far too attractive, far too charming, far too sexy for Emily's own good.

She didn't like men like him, men who could make the world jump to their wishes, men whose strength and charisma was all too obvious. Men like Marc and Alejandro Gomez, who used people for their own ends and didn't really care about them as human beings.

You thought his strength was nice when you needed it, she reminded herself, to be fair. And of course that was true. But that didn't mean she wanted to continue the acquaintance.

She slanted him a glance. He was looking at Tom, and she saw a faint softening in his features as he did so, a hint of gentleness that seemed entirely out of character.

He looked like a pirate. Or a highwayman. She had a hard time imagining him as a dreamy, non-active writer.

'What sort of books do you write?' she asked him. She might, she thought, find one some day. Read it. Remember.

'Don't say you believe me after all.'

She flushed and shrugged, remembering her scepticism last night. What if he really did write erotic stories?

'I write spy thrillers, Emily Musgrave.'

'I read spy thrillers,' Emily told him. 'I don't remember any by Sandy MacPherson or Sanford MacPherson or whatever your name is.'

'Dominic Piersall.'

She goggled. 'Dominic Piersall? *You're* Dominic Piersall?'

For the first time since she'd met him, he looked slightly embarrassed. 'On paper, I am.'

'Heavens.'

Dominic Piersall was just about the best known of the new breed of thriller writers to have come out of Britain in the post Cold-War period. Unlike the purveyors of the techno-thriller, he concentrated heavily on men and their motivations. And he did it better than anyone going as far as Emily and many other readers were concerned.

Dominic Piersall had devious clever plots that grew out of the machinations of devious, clever, all too believable characters. The biggest criticism levelled at him was that he wrote so slowly. A new book every couple of years was about all his most devoted fans could expect. Emily looked at him with awe.

Kissed by Dominic Piersall? She couldn't stifle the giggle.

'You think it's funny?'

She shook her head quickly. 'Not a bit. You're famous.'

'It's no big deal.'

'Maybe you don't think so, but . . .' She felt suddenly awkward, aware of him in yet another way. 'I didn't know. I'm sorry to have bothered you like this. I never would have, if I'd known.'

'Why? I'm not a mortal man any more? I could have declined.'

'Yes, but——'

His blue eyes nailed her. 'If you hadn't, Emily Musgrave, I'd have simply had to contrive some other way to meet you.'

The implication was too blatant to miss. It was nothing she hadn't heard from countless other men, Marc included. So why, this time, did it send a funny little quiver down her spine before she deliberately made herself stiffen and swallow hard?

'*Vous êtes là.*'

Thank God. She didn't say it, but she certainly thought it, as she gave herself a little jerk, then tore her gaze away from MacPherson's.

Startled back to the moment, Emily looked around. The taxi had stopped outside a four-storey cream stucco apartment house and the driver was looking back at her expectantly. '*Vous êtes là,*' he repeated.

'Oh—er—*oui. Merci.*'

'Is this it?' Tom looked around curiously.

But before Emily could reply, MacPherson said, 'No.' She blinked. 'But——'

He jerked his head in the direction of the cross street. 'Look. Up near the corner.'

Emily followed his gaze. She saw another taxi parked by a street-light. And in the back there sat watching them, a familiar-looking dark-haired man.

No, she thought. It couldn't be! How had he known?

She wanted to scream. To cry.

Before she could do more than draw a breath, Mac spoke rapidly to the driver in French. The driver shrugged, then grunted a response, backed the car up and shot around the corner, heading back from where they'd come.

Emily was shaking. How had he known about Guido?

She'd told no one. Had he tailed them? But he seemed to have arrived before they did. Did he have spies in her brain? Did he know every person she had ever met?

Emily felt an impotent fury rising inside her, coupled with a sensation of growing helplessness.

'What am I going to do?' And though she hated the thread of panic in her voice, she couldn't squelch it.

'Simple,' MacPherson said as he settled back in the seat beside her. 'You're coming with me.'

They couldn't afford a room at the small exclusive lake-front hotel where Mac had reserved a room. 'We'll go some place cheaper,' Emily said when the taxi pulled up out front.

But MacPherson contradicted her. 'Don't be stupid. How am I supposed to keep an eye on you if you're staying halfway across town?'

'You don't need to keep an eye on us.'

'I'm glad to hear it,' he said drily, steering her up a flight of wide stone steps even as she protested. 'Now come along, and stop worrying. I have a suite.'

'I do not intend to impose on you,' she said as he led her through the dark wooden door.

'You're not imposing. You're invited.'

'No.'

Mac stopped suddenly in the middle of the Aubusson-carpeted foyer and turned to face her. 'Got a better idea?'

The direct challenge removed what little wind was left in Emily's sails.

She had no other ideas.

She hadn't thought beyond getting to Guido's. From there, she had been certain, she could have come up with a game plan, contacted her lawyer in the States, received some advice as to how to thwart her powerful adversary.

Now she couldn't even get there without running the gauntlet set up by Alejandro Gomez.

She blinked tiredly, the days of worry and the night without sleep catching up with her all at once. MacPherson staring down at her, powerful and challenging, didn't help in the least. She simply sagged where she stood.

'Right,' MacPherson said.

And before she knew what was happening, he steered both her and Tom up a short flight of stairs to a heavy walnut door which he opened.

'In,' he commanded, and Emily found herself in a small, tastefully furnished sitting-room with tall narrow windows overlooking the lake.

The entire suite spoke not of glitz, but of elegance and quiet good taste. It was warm and welcoming, like a safe harbour in a stormswept sea. MacPherson pointed her towards a tapestry-covered wing-chair. 'Sit.'

'I'm not a dog,' she complained as she sat.

'No. Dogs mind better.'

Tom giggled, and Emily shot him a dark look.

Mac tousled the little boy's hair. 'Are you hungry?'

Tom nodded emphatically.

Mac crossed the room and picked up the phone, then spoke rapidly in French. 'Breakfast in twenty minutes, old man,' he promised when he hung up. 'In the meantime, how about a bath?'

To Emily's everlasting astonishment, Tom agreed.

While she sat in a tired stupor, he went off happily with Mac, chattering at length about the fleet of boats for the tub he had at home in Barcelona.

'This is a huge tub,' she heard Tom say to him. 'Do you have a bathtub this big?'

'Pretty close.'

'Where do you live?'

'In England most of the time. Sometimes in Spain. Now and then in Singapore. I get around.'

Emily supposed he must. His books went all over the world. The last one she'd read, a spine-tingler called *Dominos*, had moved around the Far East with the ease of someone familiar with the area. His first book, she recalled, had been set in Spain.

'In houses? Or flats?' Tom didn't care at all about MacPherson's globe-trotting activities. He loved the idea of a house with a huge garden. He'd never had one, and, to his child's mind, heaven would be a place with huge trees to climb, a room of his own with a window overlooking a lake, and a pony to ride every day after school.

Emily knew they'd never have all that. But the house was within the realm of possibility, even though it was a long way off.

'I have a little flat in Singapore. The others are houses,' MacPherson said.

'Big 'uns?'

'Monstrous old piles, both of 'em.'

'Really?' Tom sounded awed. 'Which is your favourite?'

'The one in England. It belonged to my mother's family. Six bedrooms. A big kitchen. Nice grounds. A horse paddock and plenty of room to ride. You like to ride?'

'I . . . never have,' Tom confided wistfully.

'We'll have to change that.'

Emily stiffened. How dared he get Tom's hopes up like that? She wanted to speak up, but she didn't want him to know she'd been eavesdropping.

She also didn't want to stop.

She wanted to know all she could about MacPherson.

She knew precious little so far. He was a hard man, she could tell that simply by looking at him. She didn't think he suffered fools gladly, and she wasn't quite sure why he was bothering with her. Sometimes she didn't even think he liked her. And then he kissed her!

But a man didn't have to like you to kiss you, as Emily well knew.

Maybe it had nothing to do with her. Maybe he felt sorry for Tom. It was easy enough to do—Tom was a likeable child.

She was somewhat surprised that MacPherson had gained Tom's confidence so easily. Her nephew had not, since his mother's death, been very outgoing or willing to meet new people. Emily had put it down to a fear that any new friends might be lost to him the way his mother had. She hoped he wouldn't be hurt when they went their way and MacPherson went his. It would help if MacPherson would stop promising him treats.

She was still fuming about that when he came back into the room a few minutes later.

'Don't look so happy,' he chided.

Emily made a face at him. 'I'm not.'

'Why not? You've eluded your pursuer so far. You've landed in a perfectly decent hotel suite. You're about to be fed a full English breakfast.'

'And I'm becoming more and more beholden to a tyrannical man.'

'Are you?' He rubbed his hands together. 'Oh, good.'

'You're enjoying this, aren't you?' she accused him. 'It probably goes with being a spy novelist. Rescuing damsels in distress. Plotting and conniving escapes.'

He sank down into a chair and stretched his long legs out in front of him. 'I do admit to some expertise.'

'I suppose you've rescued lots of women?'

'One or two.' He gave her a wicked grin. 'But you're the prettiest.'

Emily looked away, hating the blush she knew suffused her cheeks.

'That was a compliment,' MacPherson said. 'You're supposed to say "thank you", Emily Musgrave. You have to learn to be gracious.'

'I am gracious,' she retorted, shooting him a glare.

One sceptical brow lifted, and she remembered all the ungracious things she'd said to him over the last half a day. 'Sometimes,' she qualified.

'We'll work on it. But first we need to make some plans.'

'*We* don't need anything,' Emily said sharply. 'This is my problem.'

'Gracious, gracious,' he chided.

Emily scowled at him. She bit her thumbnail.

'It was your problem. You involved me. Now it's mine.' His tone didn't brook any argument.

Emily argued anyway. 'I never meant——'

'That wasn't you clutching my shirt, telling me you'd lost me?'

'Once! Once, for a matter of moments I involved you. That doesn't mean——'

'And this morning? Going from the train to the taxi? How about after we got to your friend's house?'

'A gentleman wouldn't harp on these things.'

'Ah, but I never claimed to be a gentleman.'

'Bully for you,' Emily muttered with stubborn bad grace. She knew she should be grateful for his help. Dammit, she *was* grateful. She just didn't want to be beholden. Especially to him. It was too dangerous, attracted as she was to him.

'Now, if you're done fussing, we need to plan,' he said mildly after a moment.

Emily pressed her lips together. 'Fine. Plan away. I'm not exactly conversant with these sorts of intrigues. I've never had occasion to be before this.'

'That's why you need me. Pay attention to a master.'

She made a face at him.

'Do you want to stay one jump ahead of your Señor Gomez or not?'

'Of course I do.'

'Then listen up. Today we can stay here, lie low, give Tom a chance to stretch his legs, give you a chance to take a nap. Don't deny you could use one,' he said when she opened her mouth to protest. 'And tomorrow we can take a bus to Chamonix.'

'Chamonix? Why Chamonix?' Emily had heard of the well-known ski and alpine mountaineering town high in the Savoyard Alps. But she'd never been there and she certainly didn't know why she should go now.

'Because it's out of the way. It's a good place to take a break, relax a little, have some fun. And because I have a place there.'

'You have places everywhere—Spain, England, Singapore...' she said without thinking.

'Doing a little eavesdropping, were you?'

She stiffened. 'Just sitting here minding my own business. You were talking loud.'

'Of course.' His knowing smile annoyed her. 'I also rent a flat in Chamonix. I ski there in winter. I use it in the summer to write.'

'Well, then, of course *you* should go there.'

'We're all going.'

'It's not necessary. You aren't obliged to us in the least. Really. We've imposed far too much and——'

'Shut up, Emily,' he suggested conversationally.

She gaped at him, then did no such thing. 'We don't need your help,' she insisted. 'Not any more, I mean,' she added hastily, because of course they already had more times than she wanted to admit.

'But I need you.'

Emily stared. Her protests stopped, her mouth hung open. 'I beg your pardon.'

She expected him to say he'd misspoken, but he only nodded gravely and repeated, 'I need you.'

'For what? Research?' she asked after a moment, her question mingled with a giddy half-laugh.

Mac shrugged. 'If you like.' He paused, his gaze catching hers, holding it. 'But there's more than that, too. And you know it.'

Time seemed suddenly to stop.

No, Emily thought. Oh, no.

But she couldn't deny it. She did know, and, if she hadn't, the look he gave her was enough to tell her exactly what he meant. It was stark and hungry and spoke of things she'd only once dared dream of. And what a disaster that had been. She looked away.

'Emily.'

She shook her head.

'You can't deny it.'

'Don't be ridiculous,' she mumbled.

'I'm not the one who's being ridiculous. You feel it, too. I know you do.'

'I . . . I don't know what you mean.'

He leaned forward, touched her cheek and chin, lifting her head so that once more their eyes met. 'Liar.'

'Just because you're a good kisser——'

He laughed. 'Thank you very much.'

'It wasn't a compliment. It was a statement of fact. I mean . . . Oh, heavens . . .' Her face was flaming.

'What are you afraid of?' MacPherson asked after a moment. 'I mean, a woman like you——'

Her head jerked up. 'What do you know about a woman like me?'

He opened his mouth, then stopped. His gaze, which had been challenging, became oddly assessing, slightly curious. The blue eyes were not quite so cold.

Emily stared at him, defiantly.

He looked down at the toes of his shoes, then back at her. 'Maybe not as much as I thought I did.'

She won the battle, not the war.

Tom hollered from the bathroom. MacPherson went to find him a towel. While he was gone, Emily breathed more easily. When he came back, she would ask him if she could use the phone to call Guido.

'Why?' he asked when she did.

'So he'll come and get me.'

'And you don't think your friend will think to check?'

'I——'

'Come on, Emily. What are you afraid of? Me? Yourself?'

'Of course not!'

'Then . . . ?'

'It's not a good idea.'

'But you don't have a better one. You wouldn't want me to think badly of you, would you? Maybe look up your friend Gomez after you've left me . . .'

'You wouldn't!'

One dark brow lifted slightly. 'How do you know what I'll do?'

'If you think for one minute I'll let you——'

'So stop me.'

She blinked.

'Come with me to Chamonix.'

Trapped. She should have seen it coming. Oh, Emily, you are so disgustingly naïve. 'I . . . I don't know if Tom will want to.'

MacPherson smiled. 'We'll ask him.'

And that, Emily knew, meant that they would be going to Chamonix.

# CHAPTER FOUR

THE day continued with the same aura of unreality with which it had begun.

Emily supposed that was because everything that was happening was so unexpected. She had thought she would be spending the day with Guido, catching up on old times, explaining about Tom, about Gomez, trying to make Guido understand what she was up to and why.

She ate and slept. Then ate again and slept some more.

MacPherson simply took over, and Emily let him.

No, that wasn't quite right. It was more that she couldn't stop him. He had a calm and logical answer for all her protests. He made her feel an idiot for making them.

And at the same time he made her feel cosseted and cared-for. She hadn't felt like that in years. All the time she'd modelled, she'd rushed about to do someone else's bidding. With Marc, she'd always tried to please. And with Mari and Tom there was no question: she was needed, so she did what was expected of her. In this last, at least, there was no hardship. She did it out of love.

But no one had done it for her.

Until now.

'Rest,' Mac had told her once they finished an enormous breakfast and he had shown her to her room. 'Take a nap. I'll take care of Tom.'

'But I——'

'You need a break. And Tom will be fine. Don't worry, I'll take care of him.'

'You mustn't take him anywhere! Gomez might——'

'I can deal with Gomez.' He didn't say how, but the tone in his voice left no doubt that he meant it.

And when he put his hand over hers, in spite of herself, she wanted to cling to it. Only because she was so tired, she thought. Only because she was at her wits' end. If she were rational, sensible, she'd run as fast as she could. But today, at least, Emily wasn't running anywhere.

'Come and lie down,' he said, beckoning her towards the bedroom.

And Emily did as he said, letting him unbuckle her sandals and slip them off, watching as he drew back the duvet on the bed.

When he waited expectantly, she sat down, knotting her hands together, then looked up at him imploringly.

'You mustn't take him out.'

'No further than the garden,' MacPherson promised, then smiled at her. 'It's private. Only guests are allowed. Your dark-haired villain isn't a guest here, Emily. I guarantee it.'

Emily looked at him mutely, still somewhat fearful, but he met her gaze steadily, determinedly. She swallowed, then nodded and bowed her head.

He squeezed her hand once more, then moved, and she felt something brush against the top of her hair, just barely touching her hair.

His hand? His *lips*?

Oh, heavens!

She looked up quickly. But he had turned away, out of the room, pulling the door shut behind him. She sat quite still for a few moments, trying to make sense of what the last eighteen hours had wrought, what a maelstrom of emotions she was experiencing. No order came from the chaos that was her mind, and so at last, confused and dazed, she had stripped off her dress and crawled under the duvet.

When she finally awoke, she knew she must have been asleep for a long time. The morning sun was gone. The room was in shadows now and the soft mutterings that had been MacPherson and Tom were silent.

She felt an instant's panic, then deliberately forced herself to relax. If something had gone awry, she would know. MacPherson would have come and told her.

Still, she got up quickly, washed her face and brushed her hair, then dressed in a pale pink T-shirt and blue cotton jumper, strapped on her sandals and went to look for them.

She didn't have to look far.

Tom was sound asleep on the small sofa, covered with a thin cotton blanket. The television was on, the volume low, but Mac was sitting at the desk, absorbed in a stack of papers.

He looked up when she opened the door. And the way he looked at her made her glance down hastily, as if she'd forgotten to put on her clothes.

He grinned, his expression knowing.

Emily lifted her chin. 'Don't let me bother you,' she said stiffly.

He stuck the papers in his briefcase and shut it, then shook his head. 'No bother.' He got to his feet and moved towards her.

She could see it again—that touch of the jungle cat— in his walk. He had a pantherish sort of grace, a sense of purpose. She could feel it, too, the sense of awareness, the almost electrical charge that seemed to arc between them.

Emily took a step back. She remembered his last touch. His lips? Her heart kicked over.

'Sleep well?' he asked her.

'Yes, thank you,' she said quickly. 'Has Tom been sleeping long?'

'An hour or so. We went out into the garden for a walk. And no, we didn't see your friend,' he added when he saw the worried look on her face. 'The concierge managed to come up with a toy boat that beat all the ones in Tom's bathtub fleet so we sailed it on the pond. Then we came back here, had a bit of lunch, then watched a football match. He nodded off. So I covered him up and managed at last to do a bit of work.'

All the while he spoke he moved closer, until he stood scant inches from her. He lifted his hand and ran it over her hair.

Emily flinched away, swallowing. 'I knew we'd disturb you.'

'You disturb me, all right,' he said, his voice husky with desire. 'But it has nothing to do with work.'

Emily gave her head a little shake and retreated to the far side of the room. 'Don't. Please.'

He followed her. 'Why not?'

'Because . . . because we hardly know each other.'

'We've spent the night together.'

'Nothing happened!'

He lifted one dark brow. 'Didn't it?' There was a wealth of meaning in his question—a challenge.

Emily's cheeks burned. Her fingers knotted together. 'You know what I mean.'

'I know. But not because we didn't want it. Isn't that true, Emily Musgrave?'

Helpless, Emily shook her head, trying to deny it.

'Ah, Emily.' His grimace was wry. 'Why can't you admit that much? I have.' And the tone of his voice made Emily think he didn't like the admission any more than she did.

She gave him a curious look. But before she could pursue it, there was a movement from the sofa and Emily turned to see Tom stretching and opening his eyes. His gaze found first MacPherson, then Emily, and he smiled.

'We sailed a boat, Em. Did Mac tell you?' he asked eagerly, sitting up.

Mac. Emily winced. Tom had certainly been won over. 'Was it fun?' She tried for interest, but not enthusiasm.

'The best. It was just like his, he said. His real one.'

Emily looked at MacPherson. He seemed suddenly to be concentrating on the television screen. 'I thought the concierge just happened to come up with a boat...'

He shrugged. 'I told him what kind to look for.'

'Mac says maybe some day I can sail on it,' Tom told her eagerly.

The way he said Tom should learn to ride a pony? 'Oh, he does, does he?' Emily said archly.

'Why not? You might be in Burnham-on-Crouch some day,' MacPherson said gruffly. 'You could come and see me.'

'I thought you lived in London.'

'Hertfordshire. But I keep my boat in Essex.'

'I see.'

'And the house in Spain is just outside Madrid. In case you're interested,' he added, giving her a mocking smile.

Emily ignored him. 'Why did you pick Spain?'

He looked at her blankly.

'I mean, why not France? Or Germany? I assume you were looking for a Continental base for the settings for your books.'

'Oh, yeah, right.' He shrugged. 'I spent some holidays in Spain when I was a boy.'

Emily tried to imagine him as a boy. Sometimes, when he grinned, she caught sight of a hint of the child he must have been. But the toughness of the man was far more obvious. He was a hard man, a determined man, and he looked it. Emily thought he looked every bit as dangerous as the spies he wrote about. She wondered if there was more than imagination in his books.

'Do you do a lot of research?' she asked him. 'Or have you lived what you write?'

'You mean, do I break codes and sneak up on people?'

'Your books are more complicated than that,' Emily protested.

He smiled. 'Thanks. To answer your question, though, I guess you could say I daydream most, but it's grounded in reality. I have to base it on fact.'

'Does that mean the next one will have something to do with sailing?' she asked.

'Yes. There's a bit of a chase, actually.' He grinned, and she saw that gleam of boyish enthusiasm once more. It was as appealing as the rest of him. Dangerouser and dangerouser, she cautioned herself.

'Wow. You wrote about this boat?' Tom's eyes were wide. 'An' I can go on it?'

'Sure,' said MacPherson at the same time that Emily, realising she was getting in deeper, said,

'I doubt we'll ever be in England.'

'But if we are?'

'You didn't think you'd ever go to Chamonix either,' MacPherson reminded her, and there was a light in his eyes again that invited further thoughts of the way she had felt at the touch of his lips, of the response he excited, of where that could lead.

Emily's fingers twisted more tightly.

'Well, Em?' Tom pressed.

'Well, Em?' Mac echoed softly, one dark brow lifted in challenge.

Oh, Emily, she asked herself, what are you getting into?

'We'll see.'

\*   \*   \*

All the way to Chamonix MacPherson was a perfect gentleman.

Of course, Emily thought wryly as she pressed her head against the glass and stared out of the window as the bus wound its way up the alpine valley, why shouldn't he be? He was getting his own way. He had commandeered her and charmed Tom. They were doing precisely what he suggested.

He'd rung for a taxi bright and early this morning, and, with little fanfare, he'd whisked them off to the *gare routière*. Emily had kept an eagle eye out for Gomez, but she hadn't seen him anywhere.

'Probably still watching Guido's,' MacPherson had said.

'Do you think so?' Emily considered calling Guido and asking, but it had been too early when they left. She'd do it later from Chamonix. Right now she listened to MacPherson continue to work his spell over young Tom.

She had protested when Tom had plopped down next to the window and looked up imploringly at Mac, asking, 'Will you sit next to me?'

'You needn't be bothered with him all the time,' she'd said.

'It's no bother,' MacPherson had protested.

And Emily had to admit that it didn't seem to be. He was, in fact, every bit as good with Tom as she could have wished. Strong. Caring. Fatherly, almost. Exactly what Tom needed.

Once more she told herself that when she got back to the States she would have to set about meeting a few men, trying to find a permanent man in her life, trying to find a father for Tom.

Clearly she'd recovered from Marc, she thought rue-fully. At least she had if her reactions to MacPherson were anything to go by!

She watched his dark head now as he leaned towards Tom and tried to sort out her reactions to him. She was attracted, there was no doubt about that. But what point was there? She wasn't a woman for one-night stands. She wanted true love, lasting love. She'd always envied David his unswerving conviction that Mari was his one and only. She'd hoped for a similar experience herself.

After what had happened with Marc, feeling sure that the rush of excitement and romance was just that and discovering her error, she'd grown sceptical and ex-tremely cautious. At least she'd thought she had. Maybe, she realised now, she hadn't met a man since who'd stirred her interest.

MacPherson did. What was it about him that was dif-ferent from all the other men who'd come into her life before and after Marc? Well, he was more attractive than most, that was certain. He wasn't pretty-boy gorgeous like some of the men she'd modelled with. But he had a sense of himself, an air about him that suggested he knew exactly who he was and what he wanted out of life. And he looked like a man who got what he wanted, too.

But there was more than power, more than strength. There had also been a hint of gentle caring that attracted Emily, too. It was so unexpected that it had caught her unawares. But it intrigued her, made her want to know more about what made him the way he was—a per-plexing combination of toughness and tenderness.

There was, too, the fact that he hadn't tried to share her bed.

Of course she'd shared her room with Tom. But MacPherson had never suggested that she not, had never pressured her to leave her nephew and come to him. And it wasn't because he wasn't interested, either. Emily knew enough about men to know when they were interested in her. MacPherson was interested. His looks, his words had told her as much.

But he wasn't pushing.

Like now. He seemed quite content to sit next to Tom. She listened now as he told the boy something about glaciers. They'd been talking non-stop since breakfast— all about alpine skiing and mountain climbing and para- penting. It was evident, from Tom's eager questions, that her nephew felt he was embarking on the holiday of his dreams.

She wanted to lean forward and insert a voice of reason. She wanted to caution Tom about expecting too much. MacPherson was offering them a hideout, a few days' respite, not a lifetime of adventure. She hoped Tom realised that.

You'd never know it from the conversation, Emily thought wearily. They seemed to have more potential plans than the Alps had peaks. Now they were talking about going to the top of the Aiguille du Midi on the *téléphérique*.

The thought made her shudder. She'd done a photo shoot once in the Italian Alps. She'd done her best, smiling gamely out of the window of the Italian version of the *téléphérique*, thanking heaven and the photogra- pher all the while that it never really went anywhere, just hovered, for the photographer's convenience, about twenty feet above the ground.

The notion of actually boarding one of those cable cars and being hoisted through mid-air to the tip of a cloud-ridden peak made Emily's stomach lurch.

'Have you gone up there?' Tom wanted to know. 'Is it scary?'

MacPherson shook his head. 'Not unless you run into a thunderstorm.'

Emily cringed.

'Have you parapented? Climbed? Skied?'

'All of the above.'

'Can I?'

'You can go up in the *téléphérique*,' Mac replied. 'And maybe we can do a bit of climbing. The skiing isn't good this late in the year, and no, you can't parapent. Your aunt would have my head.'

This last, spoken in a carrying voice, was for Emily's benefit. And she could tell from the sound of his voice that he was smiling as he said it.

Tom giggled and turned to pop his head over the back of the seat. 'Wouldn't you like to parapent, Em?'

'Jump off the tops of mountains in a parachute? No, thank you very much. I'm not that brave.'

Mac turned his head and their eyes met. Emily felt that now familiar jolt of awareness. 'On the contrary,' he said quite seriously after a moment, 'I'd say you're very brave indeed.'

Because she was standing up to Gomez? she wondered. Because she'd come to Chamonix with him? Emily wasn't sure which he meant. She only knew that the intensity of his gaze embarrassed her. 'I do what I have to,' she mumbled.

MacPherson's gaze met hers steadily. 'So do I.'

And Emily subsided into silence, wondering, as well, what he meant by that.

Their trip to Chamonix brought them back into France again. And when Emily descended from the bus she was charmed at the small bustling town nestled against the snow-covered alpine peaks.

In winter, she imagined, the pace would be considerably more frenetic. As it was small groups of people milled about, taking photos, checking the large city map, ambling down the street towards the shops and restaurants that beckoned.

Emily herself moved slowly, carefully, taking a thorough look around to confirm what she'd been hoping since they'd boarded the bus that morning—Gomez was nowhere to be seen. When she had, she allowed herself a deep breath of pure mountain air and smiled a smile of pure bliss.

MacPherson smiled, too. 'Told you so. Now relax. Come on.' He took her hand in his. 'We'll get a taxi to my flat.'

His flat was right across the Arve River in a three-storey stucco and timber building set back from the street and overlooking the fast-moving river which tumbled along behind it.

MacPherson unlocked the door and held it open, ushering them into a tiled hallway with stairs leading upwards on the right. 'No lift—sorry,' he said. 'I'm clear at the top.'

Tom led the way, bounding eagerly ahead. MacPherson followed him and Emily brought up the rear. Off the stairs on the first floor there were two doors. At the top there was only one.

'The penthouse?' Emily asked drily.

'In a manner of speaking.' He turned the key in the lock and pushed open the door, letting them in a small entryway that opened on to a sunlit, but stuffy, living-room.

Tall windows directly faced the river and, beyond it, the Mont Blanc mountain range. MacPherson crossed the room and opened the windows, letting the breeze and the sound of the river fill the room. The wind caught the curtain and blew it back, and Emily's breath caught at the stunning view.

'Two bedrooms over here.' Mac moved to the far end of the room and opened first one door and then the other. He slanted her a grin. 'Want to share with me or Tom?'

'How about you and Tom sharing,' Emily said impulsively, 'and I'll have one of my own?'

Mac shrugged. 'Fair enough.' He picked up his and Tom's duffels and headed towards one of the bedrooms.

'I was just kidding,' Emily said hastily.

'I don't mind.'

'I'd like it,' Tom said flatly.

'But——'

MacPherson turned to Tom. 'Why don't you unpack your gear into the bureau on the far side?' And when Tom went to do just that, Mac turned to Emily. 'Let him share with me. You can't hover over him forever.'

'I'm not hovering.'

'Looks to me like you are. He's a boy, not a baby. He needs a bit of space.'

'I know!'

'Well, then?' He gave her an arch look.

'I just...don't want him to bother you.'

'I'm a big boy, too. I can defend myself. How about if I assure you that I won't let him bother me. If I begin to find him obnoxious and unpleasant I'll pitch him right out on his ear.'

'He's not obnoxious!'

MacPherson grinned. 'My point exactly.'

Emily fumed under her breath.

'So, are we in agreement? If I invite him to do something, or if I say I don't mind if he does something, you will not jump in to protect me.'

'I don't protect you!'

'You try.'

'I don't want him to be a pest. I don't want either one of us to bother you. I——'

He shook his head, his expression almost rueful. 'Emily, Emily. It's all right. Relax. You're taking this far too seriously.'

'It is serious.'

A corner of his mouth quirked. 'You amaze me,' he said softly. 'I never figured...' He shook his head once again.

'Never figured what?' Emily demanded.

'That you'd be so...so...conscientious.'

'Of course I'm conscientious. I'm Tom's guardian!'

'But you're going to make yourself ill if you keep worrying about every little thing.'

'I have to,' Emily insisted.

'Do you? Is it Tom you're worried about, Emily? Or yourself?'

'*What*?' She looked at him, horrified.

'Is that why you want him in with you? As a shield?'

'Oh, for heaven's sake!' Emily turned away, hugging her arms against her breasts.

'First I thought you were a fickle witch,' MacPherson said softly. 'And for just a bit I thought you were an ice princess. But you're not, are you, Emily? You're just scared.' His voice was caressing almost, belying the challenge in his words.

'You're dreaming,' Emily said tersely.

'Am I?' He smiled. 'I wonder.'

'All right,' she said gruffly. 'He can stay in your room. For tonight.'

'And we can keep the door open between the two rooms.'

Emily looked at him, startled. 'But——'

He laughed. 'I thought you were worried about Tom.'

'Well, I——'

'Did I jump your bones last night? Or the night before?'

'No, but ...'

He winked. 'I told you, I'm a big boy, Emily. I can wait.'

'I can wait.'

The words echoed in her ears. They had been spoken so matter-of-factly, so bluntly. No 'ifs' or 'maybes'. Just 'I can wait'. As if it was inevitable.

Was it?

Emily found herself trembling at the thought. What had she got herself into—coming to Chamonix with him, moving into his flat?

What was she doing not rejecting the idea out of hand? This wasn't like her. Yet, she had to acknowledge, MacPherson didn't make her feel like herself.

He was like Marc, she tried telling herself, bowling her over, making her crazy. And of course, Marc had. But Marc had wanted her simply as a showpiece in his collection. He had wanted to possess her. Even when she'd repulsed his advances he'd persisted in his desire to marry her. But not, as she had hoped, because he honoured her principles; only because he was making real love to someone else.

MacPherson had said nothing about marriage, of course. He was talking about sex, pure and simple. She ought to be running away as fast as she could!

And why wasn't she? she asked herself.

Gomez, she thought at once. But she'd eluded Gomez now. He wasn't the reason she was hanging around now.

So what was?

The answer was harder to come by than she'd thought. Attraction? Well, yes. Curiosity? That, too. Hope for the future? That didn't seem very likely. They'd scarcely known each other two days. But there was something in the way he looked at her. Something warm and possessive, something strong and protective? Was she dreaming?

'Don't get your hopes up,' she told herself.

Heavens, she thought, she didn't even know if he was married.

She assumed he wasn't. Certainly he didn't act married.

But what did that mean? For a year she hadn't thought Howell was married, either. If he hadn't casually mentioned his daughter, she might have gone on even longer. Even then she'd assumed he was divorced until one day Howell had said, 'Bad idea, divorce. Creates too many off-shoot families. Kids get torn.'

'Did yours?' Emily had asked, and Howell had looked at her, astonished.

'I'm not divorced. Sian and I have been married twenty-four years.'

'But I've never met her.'

Howell had shrugged. 'She doesn't live in my pocket. She does her thing. I do mine.'

Emily didn't understand, but she hadn't argued with him.

Later, when she'd run to him after the fiasco with Marc, she'd cringed at the rumours she'd spawned, worried about what they'd do to his marriage. 'Howell Evans's New Bimbo', one headline had read. And 'Sian's Fed Up', blared another.

But as far as Emily knew Sian Evans went right on sculpting as she always had, oblivious to Howell's supposed transgression. And if, when she'd had a highly touted show in London a few months later, Howell didn't go, Emily had learned it wasn't because they were on the outs, though the papers claimed that. She didn't want him there, Howell had explained.

'It's her baby, not mine,' he'd told Emily when she'd called him, worried still. 'If I'm there people ask me about my photos, they try to compare us. There is no comparison. I told you, we each do our own thing. Quit fussing.'

Emily had.

Keeping Howell in mind, she thought she'd better learn a bit more about MacPherson. There was no sense in making a fool of herself over him.

She looked around MacPherson's flat for signs of feminine habitation, expecting that even if he had a wife who did her own thing she might deign to go skiing with him. But though there were a few feminine toiletries in the bathroom there were no women's clothes in the bureau, no dresses in the wardrobe.

'Looking for something?' MacPherson asked when he walked in to find her staring at the empty cabinet.

'Your wife.'

He laughed. 'Good luck.'

'I mean, I don't even know if you're married!'

'I'm not. Yet.' He grinned. 'Want to ask me anything else?'

There were a million things Emily would have liked to have asked. She shook her head. 'Not at all.'

After they were unpacked and settled in, Mac suggested a stroll around town to get a meal and buy groceries. And taking her arm, he steered her, openmouthed, down the stairs and out into the street. Tom skipped eagerly along after them.

The air was crisp and cool in the shade even in mid June. But the direct sun was warming, and Emily stopped in the middle of the small garden to sigh and stretch in the heat of its rays.

She felt fingertips on her nape, lightly massaging. She stiffened for an instant, then melted. Protest died on her lips. She sighed. Smiled. Shut her eyes.

'C'mon, Em,' Tom shouted from the road.

She opened her eyes again to find MacPherson's face very close. His cool blue eyes looked surprisingly warm, as if there were a flicker of firelight deep within them.

She swallowed.

He smiled, then dropped his hand to take hers in his. 'Come along. Let's do some exploring.'

Chamonix was a paradise for boys, big and little, with umpteen mountaineering shops which drew both Mac and Tom like magnets. Food was forgotten as they prowled through reel after reel of climbing rope, pulling and testing, then moved on to look at climbing shoes, harnesses, pitons, axes and carabiners. From the mountaineering stores they moved to the sporting goods stores, the bike shops and the ski shops.

'Oooh, look,' Tom would say when they'd left one to come face to face with another even more tempting.

'Just one more,' MacPherson promised time after time.

Emily didn't care. She might not know a carabiner from a catfish, but she was perfectly content to while away the time looking at sportswear and postcards and souvenir cowbells. It was calming just to be able to move about without looking over her shoulder, comforting to hear Tom's eager chatter and see the smile on his face.

It was a respite. But as she sat on a bench in the sunshine and watched through the window as MacPherson hunkered down to Tom's level, showing him how to tie some sort of knot, then holding the boy's hands and helping him go through the motions until he could do it himself, she found herself wishing it could be more.

When they emerged, they had a coil of rope which Tom carried in his arms as if it were a baby. He was grinning from ear to ear.

'Look, Em!' He showed it off proudly. 'We're gonna climb.'

'Hike,' MacPherson corrected before she could say a word.

She looked at him sceptically. 'You need a rope to hike?'

'Some of the trails are a bit steep. It's a precautionary measure. A tether, if you like. We thought we'd hike down from the first station of the *téléphérique*.'

Emily looked at the high, jagged snow-covered peaks, at the tiny red dot moving slowly down the cable at an angle to the rock face. Steep wasn't the word she'd have used to describe it. Her stomach felt queasy just looking at it.

Her trepidation must have showed, for Mac grinned at her. 'You're not chicken, are you, Miss Musgrave?'

She lifted her chin. 'Of course not.'

He laughed.

They found an outdoor café overlooking the Arve which served a mixed grill lunch. Tom shared his seat with the coil of rope and hugged it at every chance he got. The moment he'd finished eating he pleaded to go up that very afternoon.

'Not today,' Mac said. 'We want good weather.'

'It's sunny,' Tom protested.

'Now. But the wind will come up later and the clouds will come in.' Mac squinted upwards. 'We might even get a bit of rain.'

Emily looked at him, astonished, for the clouds, as far as she could see, were almost non-existent. But she certainly wasn't going to disagree with him. She remembered what he'd said about being stuck in a thunderstorm.

'We'll go tomorrow morning when the weather's clear.'

Tom looked as if he was going to argue further, but MacPherson fixed him with a firm look. 'Tomorrow.'

'Can I go watch the river, then?'

Emily nodded and watched him go. He looked bright and happy today, the way she wanted him to look, the way he hadn't looked in months.

She wondered if Alejandro Gomez would be pleased to know he'd accomplished so much on his nephew's behalf. The thought made her smile.

'What's funny?'

'I was just thinking about Gomez.'

'He makes you smile?'

'Not usually. Usually he makes me angry.'

MacPherson took a swallow of beer. 'Do you really think he's that much of an ogre?'

'He certainly was to his sister. He kidnapped her.'

'What!'

'Well, maybe technically he didn't, but it amounted to the same thing. The family didn't want her dating David. My brother. She was supposed to marry the man Papa picked out for her.'

'That's not unheard-of.'

'Maybe not,' Emily conceded grudgingly. 'But they were so determined. So rigid. They wouldn't even listen. When Marielena said she didn't want to marry their choice, the Gomezes didn't take no for an answer. They told her if she married David they'd disown her! And when she said she was going to marry David anyway, clever Alejandro tried to stop her from showing up at the wedding.'

'Maybe he just wanted to plead his case.'

Emily scowled. 'Whose side are you on?'

'Yours, of course. But——'

'What would you call spiriting her away the night before the wedding, taking her way off to some god-forsaken country house and trying to browbeat her all night?'

'Obviously he didn't do any good.'

'Of course not! She loved David. She told Gomez he didn't know anything about love. And he agreed with her!' Emily shook her head just the way she had when Marielena had told her about it years ago. 'Boy, is that the truth!'

She turned and watched Tom again. He was tossing pebbles into the river, hopping on first one foot, then the other.

'So what happened?' MacPherson asked finally.

'He finally saw that he couldn't change her mind. Anyway, she showed up at the ceremony flaming mad moments before it was going to begin. David was a nervous wreck. I know he thought she'd changed her mind, that the family had convinced her, but she said she never wanted to see them again. I know David felt bad that she and her brother hadn't reconciled, but you never saw anyone so relieved when she finally got there.'

In her mind's eye Emily could still see her brother's anxious face, then the heartstopping smile that had appeared when Marielena had come in the door. She smiled at the memory. 'I was so happy for both of them. They were so much in love. You could just see it on their faces. If Alejandro Gomez had bothered to look, he might have seen it too.'

MacPherson drained his glass of beer and set it on the table. His finger traced a circle in the condensation. 'And they lived happily ever after, did they?'

'They had four years. Four good years.' She swallowed against the tightness in her throat. 'And they had Tom. Yes, I think you could say they did.'

MacPherson's gaze followed her own. They watched as Tom hung over the railing, dropping pebbles, his dark hair whipped in the breeze. 'He's a very special little boy,' he said at last.

'He is. I'd die if I had to let him go. I *won't* let him go.'

'No,' MacPherson said quietly. 'I don't expect you will.'

# CHAPTER FIVE

IT WAS all very well to agree with MacPherson that Tom should spend the night with him. It was something else again to sit at the dressing-table brushing her hair in the next room and listen to the sound of Tom's high-pitched voice, then Mac's lower-pitched rumble. They were laughing, then talking some more, like old friends, bosom buddies. She wondered what they were talking about.

Tom had used to talk at length to anyone who would listen. But in the last few months, since his mother's death, he'd become much quieter.

Except today with MacPherson. Today he'd been the old Tom, chattering a mile a minute, bounding ahead, then running back to share some titbit of information, some fascinating idea he'd just thought of. And every other word seemed to have been 'Mac'.

'Mr MacPherson,' Emily had tried belatedly to insist upon. MacPherson had rolled his eyes.

Tom had simply said, 'He likes me callin' him Mac.' Emily could see that making an issue of it would never work.

'Just don't get your hopes up, little one,' she whispered now, hearing over the running water a high-pitched giggle and Tom's exaggerated, 'Oh, Mac!'

Then, all of a sudden, the door to her room flew open and Tom hurtled through.

He was ready for bed, hair damp, face scrubbed, and he flung himself on her, a grin on his face. 'I came to kiss you goodnight,' he announced.

She looked up to see MacPherson right behind him.

Emily dropped her brush and caught Tom to her, using his wriggling six-year-old self to cover as much of her as her skimpy nightgown did not.

Logically she knew that if Mac had seen her on the cover of half a dozen magazines he had certainly seen more of her than she was showing now. But it wasn't the same. Those were posed, impersonal, two-dimensional, and, as far as Emily was concerned, not really *her*. This was.

She gave Tom a quick smacking kiss. 'Goodnight,' she said, curling her long bare legs under the cotton of her nightgown.

Mac watched, grinning. 'Do I get a goodnight kiss too?'

Emily made a face at him, but Tom beamed. 'Yeah,' he chimed in. 'Mac, too.'

'Tom! For goodness' sake!'

'You always made me kiss Gloria.'

'Gloria is a friend. It's not the same thing.'

'Mac is a friend, too, you said so,' Tom reminded. 'An' he doesn't smell like paint thinner.'

MacPherson winced. 'A backhanded compliment, I think.' Still, he didn't seem averse to capitalising on it. He tapped a spot on his cheek and grinned at Emily. 'Just a small one. Right here. I won't tax your strength.'

'You kissed him at the train station,' Tom reminded her.

'That was different.'

Tom looked at her, wide-eyed. 'Oh? How?'

Explanations, Emily knew from experience, would do no good at all. She might just as well kiss him and get it over with.

Besides, there was a certain truth to the old quotation about 'protesting too much'. 'Fine.' She set Tom on the floor, got up, still keeping as much of herself covered as possible, and pecked MacPherson on the cheek.

'There.' She gave a brisk nod. 'Satisfied.'

'Yup.' Tom beamed.

'Not a chance,' Mac murmured. He took Tom by the shoulders and steered him towards his room. 'But I guess it'll have to do. For now.' And with a wink over his shoulder, he chivvied Tom out of the room.

Emily sank down on the bed again, her lips still tingling from the brief contact with Mac's faintly bristly cheek. Get control of yourself, she mentally admonished. But it took more than one deep breath to restore her equilibrium.

'He's not that handsome,' she muttered to herself.

But handsome wasn't the issue. He attracted her. He was strong and capable, yet solicitous and kind, sexy yet caring. A lethal combination. But would it go anywhere?

She didn't know.

Mac hadn't shut the door when he and Tom left, and Emily got up to shut it now. She paused, doing so, caught by the conversation.

'You really think we can hike tomorrow?' Tom was asking.

'If the weather's good.'

There was a slight pause. Then, 'I'm glad,' Tom said. 'I didn't think I'd ever get to go hiking. I thought you needed a dad for that.'

Emily's breath caught in her throat.

'You were very little when he died, weren't you?' she heard Mac ask him.

'Three. I 'member some things. He used to ride me on his shoulders. And sometimes on the weekends we'd go out and buy the newspaper and a *coca* and bring them back and crawl into bed again with Mommy.' Tom's voice wavered a little. 'They'd read the paper and we'd all eat the *coca* and drink coffee, and tell jokes and laugh.'

'You must miss him a lot.'

'Yeah.' Tom's voice was a bare whisper. 'I want him back. I want my mom back, too.'

There was a long moment of silence, then the sound of a sob, followed by another. Emily started to open the door, then heard Mac move.

'Come here,' he said and she heard a shuffling noise and then what sounded like the sobs being muffled into his shirt.

'Oh, hell, Tom,' he muttered. 'Oh, God, I'm sorry.'

Emily froze, her hand on the door-handle. She should go in, take Tom in her arms and comfort him. Right after his mother's death, he'd sobbed and sobbed. But over the past couple of months he'd come out of it, looking forward, not back. And Emily had felt he was getting over it.

Now she felt as if no time had passed at all. She thought she should intervene, yet wondered about the wisdom of it. He hadn't confided this to her, but to Mac.

More muffled sniffles, then she heard, ''S'OK. 'M OK,' and Mac promising,

'You will be. I swear it.'

Tom hiccupped. 'I don' usually cry,' he mumbled.

'It's all right to cry.'

There was a pause. 'Do you? Sometimes?' Tom's voice was still a little croaky.

Emily waited, as curious as Tom. She couldn't imagine Sandy MacPherson crying.

'Yes.'

'Did you when your parents died?' Tom asked him.

'I did when my father died. My mother's still alive. But she has a bad heart.'

'Is she gonna die?'

'I hope not. It worries me.'

'Yeah,' Tom said after a moment, and Emily knew he was remembering his own worries, settling down now that he realised they weren't unique. 'I know what you mean. Do you got brothers and sisters?'

There was a pause. Then, Mac said quietly, 'No. I don't have anyone but my mother now.'

'I'm lucky. I've got Emily. I wouldn't have nobody if I didn't have Emily.'

Emily felt her cheeks heat and was conscious once more of eavesdropping. Still she couldn't move away.

'What about your mother's family?' she heard Mac ask.

'They don't like me.'

'What do you mean, they don't like you?' Mac sounded offended.

'They didn't like my daddy. They didn't want my mommy to marry him.'

'How do you know that?'

'My mommy said so.'

There was a long silence. Emily felt, if not pleased, at least vindicated. If Mac had thought she was exaggerating about the lack of rapport between the Gomez family and her brother and sister-in-law, he would know now that she wasn't the only one to feel that way.

'I think they were pretty dumb, don't you?' Tom said candidly.

'Yes,' Emily heard MacPherson reply, 'yes, I do.' There was a pause. Then, 'Here. Blow.' Emily heard Tom give a mighty blow of his nose. 'Better?' Mac asked.

'Uh-huh.'

'Time for lights-out, then.'

'Emily always reads me a story.'

'Want me to call her?'

'Not tonight,' Tom said matter-of-factly. 'She'll see I been crying and she'll be sad. I don't want Emily to be sad. So, will you? Read it, I mean?'

'If you're sure...'

Was that hesitation in MacPherson's voice?

'You know how, don't you?' Tom sounded momentarily worried.

MacPherson laughed. 'I write 'em, remember?'

'That's right. I'll get it out of my bag.' Emily heard him bounce down on to the floor and cross the room, rummage through his duffel and come back. 'I'm glad you're Emily's friend, Mac,' he said as he bounced on to the bed, making the springs creak. 'I like you.'

And before she eased the door completely shut and tiptoed back to her bed, Emily heard Mac say softly, 'I like you, too.'

The morning dawned bright and still. A perfect day to go to the Aiguille du Midi, according to Mac. As far as Emily was concerned, no day was perfect to dangle so far above the world in what seemed to her a very tiny cable-car compartment.

'You don't have to come if you don't want to,' Mac said. 'I can take him by myself.'

'No.' She shook her head, adamant. 'I'm going. I need to.'

Emily couldn't have said precisely why she felt so strongly about it. It wasn't as if she feared that Alejandro Gomez was going to be waiting at the top of the Aiguille du Midi, ready to snatch Tom out of Mac's grasp and she had to be there to prevent it. But it did have something to do with Gomez, something to do with what she'd overheard last night between Mac and Tom, something to do with Tom's protecting her.

It should be the other way around, she'd thought then. She should be protecting and caring for Tom. That was what this flight into France was all about. So Gomez would forget them and they could live in peace together.

But obviously he didn't intend to forget them. He had pursued them to Geneva. If he'd momentarily lost them, it only meant that his physical pursuit had been stymied. He still had legal recourse, or he must think he did.

There would be a fight now, Emily knew that for certain. Emily didn't like confrontations. She didn't like battles. But if caring for Tom meant a battle, she'd do it. So she needed to start facing her fears, and conquering them.

She was starting this morning by going up in the *téléphérique*.

They had to wait nearly an hour until their number was called to board the cable-car. The whole while Emily watched nervously as the small red cars lurched up out of the station and edged their way up the face of the mountain.

'You sure about this?' Mac asked in her ear as she stood, chewing the inside of her cheek and mentally distributing her worldly goods.

She ventured a fleeting smile. 'I'll be fine. It's just nerves.'

All the same she was grateful he was there to keep an eye on Tom, because she was hardly capable of doing it. It was all she could do, when the time came, to allow herself to be herded through the station and into the waiting car where she stood pressed against a window, one hand gripping one of the uprights, her eyes fixed on the mountain ahead.

She felt strong fingers lace through hers and Mac's shoulder hard against her own. 'I've got an idea,' he whispered in her ear, and she could hear the smile in his voice. The cable-car lurched and began its ascent.

'What's that?' Emily managed, but her voice cracked.

'You need to take your mind off it. Think about something more important.'

What, Emily wondered, could be more important than concentrating every single thought on making sure the cable didn't break?

'This.' And Mac's warm lips closed over hers, a firm arm came around her, pulling her hard against a strong body.

It could have been the altitude, or her fear of heights, or any number of things. But whatever it was, Emily's world shrank, her ears rang, and her gasp for breath was cut short.

Her hand loosed the upright and came to clutch his jacket, her fingers curling into the soft cotton as she clung to him desperately, lost in the heady warmth and hunger of his touch.

'You're missin' the best part,' Tom complained at her elbow.

No, Emily thought. Not true. Nothing in the world could be better than this.

The impatient unrelenting shoving at her back was her first indication that the earth had stopped moving. Her earth hadn't.

But a cleared throat, a muttered, '*Pardon, mademoiselle,*' followed by a definite jostle as the door opened, brought her back to reality.

Blushing she stammered, '*Oui, monsieur. Pardon.*' And still gripped in Mac's embrace, she was shuffled off the cable-car and on to another.

'Wha——?' she began.

But the kiss began again, taking up right where it had left off.

'Ma—mmmm.' Her protest was swallowed by his lips. She heard titters, she heard murmurings. She didn't care. She cared only for MacPherson.

It was only when the cable-car jolted once more and the pushing and muttering began again and MacPherson took a small step back and allowed a millimetre of space between their lips that she breathed again.

'Maybe that wasn't such a great idea.' His voice was hoarse, and she noticed for the first time the tide of colour that had crept into his face and the tell-tale pulse hammering in his temple.

'It got me up here,' she said in a voice only slightly more shaky than his.

MacPherson looked around them at the crowd, at the walkway that spanned the gorge between two parts of the peak. 'Swell,' he muttered. 'Rather it'd got you into bed.'

Emily, feeling as safe as ever she was likely to at three thousand, eight hundred and forty-two metres, grinned at him. 'You're quite a Boy Scout.'

'Aren't I, though?' he said wryly.

'Can we go to the top, Mac? Can we?' Tom pestered.

'To the top?' Emily echoed faintly. 'What for pity's sake is this?'

'Close,' Tom said and pointed towards the lift that would take them even higher.

'Why not?' Mac said wryly. 'We've come this far.'

Emily, refusing to look down, allowed Mac to steer her across the bridge that spanned the crevasse between the building housing the *téléphérique* station and a restaurant-cum-gift-shop and the topmost point where Tom was headed. At least she was upright and functioning. In this instance she would take her victories where she could find them.

They queued for the lift, then were ushered in, packed like sardines and the doors closed. The lift began to rise. Ordinarily lifts were not a problem.

It must have been the altitude, she thought afterwards. Or the claustrophobic sensation of sharing a cramped space with eleven other people. She didn't know what else could have possessed her to croak, 'I could use another kiss.'

MacPherson stared at her. 'Is this torment or is this torment?'

'If I have to suffer, you do, too.'

'What a way to go,' he groaned, and once more his lips closed over hers.

It was amazing how well it worked.

'My dad and mom used to kiss like that. Maybe you two should get married,' Tom said.

That and the sudden stop of the lift brought Emily back to reality with a thump. She pulled back, mortified, her hand going to her lips. 'Tom!'

But MacPherson only smiled. 'There's an idea.'

Emily swallowed, staring at him.

He shrugged equably at her lack of response. 'Ah, well. It was a thought.'

He seemed as unfazed by the idea as Emily was stunned—not by the idea so much as by his apparent equanimity. Could he possibly be interested in more than a simple flirtation?

She pulled away from him and deliberately walked over to the edge of the platform, gripping the railing until the vertigo passed and she dared open her eyes to the panoramic vista before her.

The French Alps from above were even more dramatic than they were seen from below. There was a wildness to them, a grandeur, that Emily had never found in the mountains of her native America. The Rockies, daunting though they were, seemed tame by comparison.

And, as long as she didn't look straight down at mountaineers no bigger than pin-pricks picking their way along a snow- and ice-covered trail, she could handle it, even marvel at the beauty of it.

It was, in fact, she thought, easier to handle than the heady notion of marrying MacPherson. Why hadn't he rejected it? Why had he looked at her with the speculative look in his eye?

'Glad you came after all?' Mac's voice said in her ear, startling her.

'It was worth the trip,' she said without thinking.

'Thank you. I think,' he added wryly, and Emily, remembering suddenly just what she had spent the trip doing, laughed and blushed again.

'Don't do that,' he said.

'Do what?'

'Blush. It plays havoc with my hormones.'

'It's the altitude.'

He smiled. 'That's what you think.'

They spent another half-hour on the top, and Emily didn't know which made her giddier, the altitude or the look in MacPherson's eyes. She was glad when they took the lift down and stopped in the restaurant and gift shop where Tom bought a patch of the Aiguille du Midi for Emily to sew on his jacket and Mac bought them ham sandwiches and hot chocolate.

'A man can't live on kisses alone,' he said in Emily's ear.

She flushed and gave him a little push, and he grinned. 'You're doing it again. Blushing.'

'Where're we gonna sit?' Tom demanded. 'All the tables are taken.'

'Sit here, sweetie,' said a distinctly American voice. A sixtyish woman patted a place at the long Formica table she was sharing with three other women.

Tom looked at Emily, who nodded. 'Thank you very much,' she said, slipping into a seat next to the woman, pointing Tom to the chair across the table. Mac, carrying the tray of drinks and sandwiches sat down next to him.

'I'm Maggie Copeland from Dallas.'

'Emily Musgrave,' Emily said, because the woman was obviously expecting a response.

'I'm Tom,' Tom said through a huge bite of his sandwich.

Maggie Copeland smiled at him. 'So nice to see families here,' she said to Emily. 'Can't understand families who leave their kids at home and go gallivanting all over the world without 'em. Walter and I used to take ours everywhere, open their eyes, let them see the world. Glad to see you agree.'

Emily nodded, her mouth full.

'Definitely,' MacPherson said. Emily shot him a look of consternation.

Maggie beamed. 'You sound British, but your wife sounds as if she's from the States.'

'She is,' MacPherson said while Emily made strangling noises.

Maggie Copeland looked again at Tom. 'Just the one little boy?'

'For the moment.' MacPherson gave Maggie Copeland a devilish wink.

All the women at the table let out a chorus of appreciative cackles. Emily choked on her sandwich.

Maggie reached over and patted her hand. 'Be glad he's still so interested, dear,' she counselled. 'So many husbands are busy looking the other way.'

Emily swallowed. At last. 'He's not——'

'Of course he's not,' Maggie said emphatically. 'Nor is he ever likely to. My Walter was just the same. The marrying kind. The faithful kind. You can see it in their eyes.'

Emily would have loved to look into MacPherson's eyes at that moment, desperate to know just what exactly it was that Maggie saw there. But there was no way she could bring herself to do it. She buried her face in her cup of hot chocolate.

'Must go. Come along, girls,' Maggie pushed her chair back. She gave Emily's shoulder a squeeze. 'All the best to you. And I must say, I hope you have half a dozen more.' She paused and gave Tom another look, then turned back to Emily. 'You two make handsome kiddies.'

It was a full minute before Emily could bring herself to look at MacPherson. When she did, he was grinning like the Cheshire Cat. 'You could have corrected her,' she said accusingly.

'Why? She would have been disappointed and embarrassed if she'd found out otherwise after making her assumptions. Besides, did you really want to explain everything to her?'

'No, of course not.'

'Well, then...?'

Emily sighed. She couldn't explain it without sounding like an idiot. How did you say to a man that you had been entertaining such thoughts yourself, that the idea was surprisingly tempting? 'It made me uncomfortable,' she said finally.

'What did? The idea of being married? Or being married to me?'

'Don't be silly.'

'I'm not.' He shifted in his chair, his mouth curving into a hint of a smile. 'Tom suggested it, if you recall.'

'Tom's a child! Children say all sorts of silly things.'

'Did you think it was silly?'

'I . . .' She wished she hadn't finished her sandwich so quickly. She would have loved to have her mouth full right now.

'Just for the record, do you plan to get married some day?'

'Of course, when the right man comes along.'

'What if he already has?'

The altitude was making her ears ring, making her hear words she didn't believe she could possibly have heard. She swallowed desperately, trying to clear her ears, trying to make sense of the words she thought he'd just said. What if he already had? Did that mean . . .?

'I—I . . . haven't considered it,' she lied.

'Consider it, then.' He pushed back his chair and stood up. 'And let me know. Ready to go?' he asked Tom, who had been watching as another little boy shredded his lunch on to his plate.

'Can I look at those key chains over there first?'

'Why not?' Mac took his hand and started towards the counter, then stopped and looked back over his shoulder. 'Take your time,' he said to Emily, then smiled. 'Enjoy your lunch.'